*Hoover Institution Publications*

# Food and Agriculture
# in Communist China

# Food and Agriculture in Communist China

*By*

John Lossing Buck
Owen L. Dawson
Yuan-li Wu

*Published for*
The Hoover Institution
on War, Revolution, and Peace
Stanford University, Stanford, California
*by*

Frederick A. Praeger, Publishers
NEW YORK • WASHINGTON
Pall Mall Press
LONDON

The Hoover Institution on War, Revolution, and
Peace, founded at Stanford University in 1919 by
Herbert Hoover, is a center for advanced study and
research on public and international affairs in the
twentieth century. The views expressed in its publications are entirely those of the authors and do not
necessarily reflect the views of The Hoover Institution.

FREDERICK A. PRAEGER, PUBLISHERS
111 Fourth Avenue, New York, New York 10003, U.S.A.
77–79 Charlotte Street, London W.1, England


Published in the United States of America in 1966
by Frederick A. Praeger, Inc., Publishers

Library of Congress Catalog Card Number: 65–28286


Printed in the United States of America

# Contents

# INTRODUCTION

From the time the Communist regime was established in mainland China in 1949 and up to 1960, Peking followed an agricultural policy which was aimed at self-sufficiency in food. Reversal of this policy in 1960 was a matter of political necessity which grew out of a severe food shortage affecting not only localities of heavy concentrations of population, but the armed forces as well. However, in spite of the continuation of grain imports up to this writing (end 1964), one is left with the strong impression that self-sufficiency in food supply remains one of the major objectives the Communist regime hopes to attain before too long.

There is, *a priori,* no compelling reason why a country must try to feed itself with food grown in its own borders. It is true that considerations of power politics may counsel against dependence upon imports of food from external sources, which are susceptible to peremptory interruption. Yet even this primarily military and political argument may have to be reexamined if the nature of potential conflicts is no longer necessarily characterized by blockade and attrition,* such as the Sino-Japanese War and the Communists' civil war with the Nationalist Government.

The really telling argument for pursuing self-sufficiency in food is that under present Chinese conditions it may be a more economical way to allocate resources. If food has to be imported, other nonfood items would have to be exported. Not only is there a problem of developing large export

---

* One may raise the question whether Communist China's leaders are still thinking in terms of wars of attrition in the future and, if so, whether this frame of mind is based on a rational evaluation of probabilities.

markets for these goods, but other imports—especially industrial machinery and raw materials that cannot be produced at home, or produced in adequate quantities—may have to be sacrificed in order to permit the financing of food imports. Besides, resources which would be used more intensively in order to produce more food may not be suitable for producing other exportable products or import substitutes for the industrial sector of the economy. An exception to this generalization may be found in the export of food of a higher unit value in return for the import of cheaper and possibly coarser food products—for example, export of rice and import of wheat and barley. But the general state of the imperfect transferability of resources from food grain production to the production of industrial goods either for domestic use or for export, problems of export promotion for both agricultural and other products, and the common factors that are necessary conditions for the expansion of production of both food and other, nonfood items—all these considerations seem to argue in favor of a policy to produce more food domestically.

Even at a time when Communist China's first explosion of an atomic device has focused attention on the military implications of developments in the Chinese mainland, an understanding of Peking's food policy is still very crucial and opportune. Not only must the expanding Chinese population be fed, but the decision whether or not to pursue an active and expanding program of nuclear development may affect Communist China's ability and speed of progress to become self-reliant in modern industry. The latter would, in turn, affect the intensity of the need felt by Chinese planners to become self-sufficient in food and to curtail net food imports. An expanded nuclear development program may conceivably preempt so much of the country's scientific and engineering manpower that its greater than usual shortage in other industrial sectors, with respect to all of the functions of research, development, and production in which such manpower must be engaged, may retard self-sufficiency in these other sectors and prolong, as well as intensify, dependence upon imports. The greater the dependence on industrial imports, the greater the pressure to curtail food imports. On the other hand, to the extent that nuclear development can be made instrumental in extending Communist China's political control to certain food-surplus areas in Asia, the Chinese Communists may believe that a more active nuclear program could help resolve some of the economic bottlenecks.

Probably as much as 85 per cent of the present caloric intake of the Chinese population is derived from food grain crops. Discussion of the food situation in Communist China and of its prospects must, therefore, begin with a discussion of the supply of food grains. In order to make such a discussion meaningful and to enable us to make certain projections, several prerequisites must in turn be present. First, we must know what the present situation is. There must be some fairly accurate idea of the levels of current production and consumption. Secondly, we must be able to identify the conditions under which increase in production would be possible. We must, of course, be able to estimate the order of magnitude of such feasible increases. Thirdly, we must make an effort to evaluate the present policy of Communist China and the environment within which it operates, in order to determine whether the necessary conditions for such an expansion can, and are likely to, be present at all. These are no mean tasks. But, like all such studies, a beginning must be made.

The present volume of four essays represents a cooperative effort. The authors' purpose is to provide some clues to answering the questions raised above. The authors would not be so bold as to claim that they know even the majority of the answers. It is their hope, however, that these papers will serve as a catalyst of a more intensive research effort in this field by identifying the gaps of present information, as well as by removing some of the current misconceptions.

The first essay by John Lossing Buck constitutes the groundwork in Chinese agricultural statistics. It examines both pre-Communist and Communist statistics of cultivated land, crop hectares, the multiple cropping index, and the various concepts of yields, production, and consumption in their historical context. It presents the reader with a historical basis for comparison and, by imparting a sense of continuity, helps him to become more discerning in evaluating Communist Chinese statistics. For instance, the study reveals certain inaccuracies in official data for the pre-Communist period, which are apparently used by the Communists in the initial year in their 1949–58 series of statistics which indicated continuous increases each year. Dr. Buck demonstrates that by the Communists' own data, average production was significantly lower for 1949–58 than for 1931–37 or for 1929–33, although the actual average production may have been different, even higher. The paper also shows how estimates of production need not be a matter of pure guess work on the production side; a number of cross-checks and tests are available. At the same time, it is also shown that in checking production data by estimates of consumption, a large number of variables are involved so that accuracy becomes a function of the judicious choice of the key variables. The size of rations, the size and age composition of the population, the proportion of food versus non-food uses, the degree of waste and loss at different stages, the composition of the rations and the crops, the milling factors used, and changes in stock are among the many factors involved. The complexity of the task and the difficulties involved in estimation should serve both as a warning and as a challenge to those who are interested in this craft.

In the second essay, by Yuan-li Wu, attention is divided

between two principal tasks. In the first place, an attempt is made to determine the causes of inaccuracy in Communist China's statistical reporting on foodcrop production. Adjustments are then made on the basis of consumption estimates involving the use of the many variables enumerated above. An "adjusted model" of Communist China's grain production is then presented and a long-term trend is projected on the basis of the model. It is suggested that such a trend line, which may be modified as more information on the environmental factors mentioned in the first essay becomes available, might serve as a basis of projections of production increases —which must be attained through significant technological and institutional changes—in relation to consumption requirements.

In the second place, the essay attempts to contrast the two different approaches to the improvement of agriculture in mainland China. The one stresses the primary need to increase production by increasing the size of the farm business. The other emphasizes the primary importance of distribution as a means of increasing production. In stressing the need for such institutional changes as land redistribution, collectivization, and the formation of the communes, the Communist regime has essentially followed the second approach, and it has found that its doctrinaire interpretation of this approach has militated against its other efforts to increase production. A dilemma is posed for the Communist leaders, and no solution appears in sight.

The production trend projected in the second essay is predicated upon gradual improvements on the existing technological base which is still largely that of traditional agriculture. To break away from such a trend, a far greater application of capital will be needed. Such applications, often involving new technologies, may be introduced in a number of ways. A major factor would be the increased use of chemical fertilizers, which must be accomplished by the more extensive and wise utilization of water. The demand for chemical fertilizers, given certain input-output relationships and the estimated availability of organic fertilizers, and the cost and availability of such supplies constitute the subject matter of the third essay. This is then followed by an examination of the extent and effectiveness of irrigation in the pre-Communist and Communist periods in the fourth essay. Both essays are by Owen L. Dawson whose two decades of experience in Chinese agriculture enable him to speak with an expertness possessed by few others. It is, of course, recognized that factors other than chemical fertilizers and use of water could affect output sharply. Not the least of these are the institutional arrangements discussed in the second essay, not to mention other technical factors. Yet the last two essays probably touch upon the core of the technical problems and, in any event, must suffice for the present volume.

Each author wishes to acknowledge the help of the others in preparing their individual manuscripts. While they may not be in full agreement on every detail, they are in general agreement on the findings.

In addition, Dr. Buck wishes to acknowledge with gratitude assistance for materials from Dr. Leslie T. C. Kuo and Chong Twanmo and helpful suggestions from Dr. A. B. Lewis and Dr. Leonard A. Maynard. He is above all greatly indebted to his wife and daughter for their assistance in the preparation of the manuscript. Mr. Dawson, on his part, wishes to record his gratitude to Dr. C. L. Tung, especially for research on organic fertilizer in China, to N. Guidy for the charts, to Dr. John Aird of the Census Bureau for advice on population estimates, and to Dr. D. Kessing of the Institute of Defense Analysis, among others, for many helpful suggestions.

As for the author of this introduction, he is particularly grateful for the opportunity to work together with two of the foremost experts on Chinese agriculture. Our collaboration began in 1960, after a panel discussion on Communist China's food production at an annual meeting of the Association for Asian Studies in New York. Through the years the manuscripts underwent a number of drafts and changed considerably in coverage. Three of the four essays first were edited by Dr. Buck; Mr. Dawson's study on chemical fertilizers, originally intended for separate publication, was finally incorporated in the present volume in order to make its contents available to the reader at the same time. Acknowledgement is gratefully made especially to Grace Wei-pan Hsiao for her assistance both in preparing the author's own essay and in the assembly of the entire manuscript. Needless to say, the author is greatly indebted to his wife and daughter for their assistance and indulgence.

*December*
*1964*

Food and Agriculture
in Communist China

# Food Grain Production in Mainland China Before and During the Communist Regime

By reference to records of production during the period prior to the Communist regime, one may arrive at an objective evaluation of the reliability of Communist food grain statistics and claims of progress which have been accepted by many people as evidence of progress. This comparison is presented not only for an understanding of the 1949–58 claims, but also as a benchmark for the assessment of any future data issued for mainland China. A compelling reason for this analysis is the Republic of China's inadvertently incorrect official production data for 1931–37 upon which the Communists apparently based their initial figure for 1949.

## I. SOURCES OF DATA PRIOR TO THE COMMUNIST REGIME

There are two main sources of data for 22 provinces of pre-Communist China that can be used for comparative purposes. One is the statistics of the National Agricultural Research Bureau (NARB) of the Republic of China for 1931–37, quoted by Shen.[1] The other is the three-part *Land*

[1] T. H. Shen, *Agricultural Resourees of China* (Ithaca, N. Y.: Cornell University Press, 1951) , with particular reference to quotations in appendices from the National Agricultural Research Bureau on production and crop hectares statistics.

*Utilization in China* * field study carried out under the auspices of the University of Nanking, 1929–33.[2] Each of these sources gives objective data without attempting to make the statistics agree with any economic, political, or social philosophy.

In addition to these two important sources, two others are included for comparative purposes. One of historical interest is the *Statistical Monthly*,[3] which supersedes the first attempt in *An Estimate of China's Farms and Crops* [4] to determine the amount of cultivated land and production of various crops, as explained in note (2) to appendix at Table 2. The other source is the Combined Estimates of "per cent of crop area" in various crops obtained by NARB reporters and by *LU* enumerators for a total of 737 hsien, 830 localities, 22 provinces (see *LU-A*, pp. 211–212, Table 3). The estimates by *LU* enumerators are independent of the *LU* Farm Survey data. The chief contribution of this source is an additional estimate of crop area for each crop, which makes possible the computation of production from *LU* yields.

* Hereafter, this study in its entirety will be referred to as "*LU*"; the three parts, "*LU-A*," "*LU-B*," and "*LU-C*" respectively.

[2] John Lossing Buck, *(A)*, *Land Utilization in China* (Chicago: University of Chicago Press, 1937 [out of print]; Nanking, China: University of Nanking, 1937 [out of print]). This publication includes analyses of data obtained from the following field survey studies: (1) Farm Survey of hectares and production for each crop, density of population, and other pertinent information for each of 16,786 farms in 168 localities, 22 provinces. (2) Food Consumption Survey for 2,727 farm families of 17,351 persons in 136 localities, 21 provinces. (3) Population Survey of 38,256 farm families in 101 localities, 17 provinces. *(B)*, *Land Utilization in China-Statistics* (Chicago: University of Chicago Press, 1937 [out of print]; Nanking, China: University of Nanking, 1937 [out of print]). A summary of data from farms and families on topics in Part *A* above, by localities, *hsien*, and provinces, grouped by each of the Eight Agricultural Areas, the two major regions of wheat and rice, and total for the Eight Areas. *(C)*, *Land Utilization in China—Atlas* (Chicago: University of Chicago Press, 1937 [out of print]; Nanking, China: University of Nanking, 1937 [out of print]). Important information obtained in Parts *A* and *B* is presented in large maps.

[3] Directorate of Statistics, National Government, *Statistical Monthly* (Nanking), combined issues for Jan. and Feb., 1932.

[4] C. C. Chang, *An Estimate of China's Farms and Crops* (Nanking, China: University of Nanking, Dec. 1932).

### *The National Agricultural Research Bureau (NARB) Estimates*

The NARB crop data (hereafter referred to as "NARB Estimates") are based on the reports of several thousand voluntary crop reporters throughout the 22 provinces. These persons each year reported the condition of crops during the growing season and also the harvested yields per *mow* of each important crop. The NARB multiplied these yields by the acreage in each crop to obtain the total production. The percentage of cultivated land in each crop was determined in a special survey. These percentages were multiplied by the NARB figure for cultivated land, 65.8 million hectares for 22 provinces, to obtain the area of each crop. Unfortunately, this land figure omitted a large amount of cultivated land, as will be explained later.

The 1932 NARB study of food consumption by farm families (hereafter referred to as "NARB Food Survey") also provides information for checking NARB Estimates of production with consumption.[5]

### *Land Utilization in China*

The *LU* study has two specific parts respectively denoted as "*LU* Farm Survey" and "*LU* Food Survey." Data for the entire study were obtained from several sources: farm and farm household data from farmers for the land they farmed, and from their own households; food consumption data from farm families; population data from farm families and house-

[5] National Agricultural Research Bureau, "A Study of the Consumption of Staple Food Products in Rural China," *Crop Reports*, VI, No. 10 (Oct. 15, 1938), P. 115. This study summarizes 3,278 usable returns from 1,042 *hsien* in 22 provinces. See also Tang and Chang, "A Calculation of the Rural Dietary from Crop Reports," *Chinese Journal of Physiology*, Vol. XIV, No. 4, 1939.

holds; and other sources. Information was collected by
trained graduates of the College of Agriculture, University
of Nanking. Localities for study were selected after a survey
of their representativeness of a larger area. Data in schedules
were cross-checked for accuracy.

The information was tabulated by the averages for 100
farms in each locality and summarized for each of the Eight
Agricultural Areas, for the Wheat Region and the Rice
Region, and for all the Eight Agricultural Areas of the same
provinces as included in NARB Estimates. Actually, the
Eight Agricultural Areas included slightly less area than the
22 provinces, but the total area may be considered the same
as that of the 22 provinces, and the terms are used synony-
mously. The names of the provinces appear in the glossary
under "Provinces."

The purpose of the *LU* study was to show relationships
between natural or basic factors, type of land use, farm population density, and success in use of land in terms of production, standard of living, and nutrition. Thus, the *LU* study
contains information which makes possible the cross-checking
of cultivated area and production with population and food
consumption in terms of national totals. This monograph
undertakes for the first time such a compilation of national
totals with the immediate purpose of comparison with other
pre-Communist periods and Communist data.

### Comparative Data for 22 Provinces and Mainland China

The labels "NARB Estimates," "NARB Revised," "Combined Estimates," and "*LU* Farm Survey" are used to specify
that data are from the 22 provinces. The label "NARB Revised" is used for *LU* corrections of NARB Estimates because of omission of cultivated land. The labels "NARB
Estimates-M," "Combined Estimates-M," and "*LU* Farm
Survey-M" are used to indicate the inclusion of additional
data for Manchuria, Sikang, and Sinkiang to represent main-

land China. The *Statistical Monthly* data are for mainland China, although they are incomplete for some areas (see note (2), Appendix Table 2).

## II. COMMUNIST STATISTICS FOR MAINLAND CHINA

In Communist China, the methods of obtaining and compiling data vary for different periods, as described—not too clearly—in the *Handbook of Agricultural Statistical Work.*[6] Standardized national general reports on agricultural production were initiated in 1953, but it is not clear how data were compiled in the previous years, 1949–52. It is stated that forms were issued in 1953 for periodic reports from provinces, autonomous regions, and municipalities. These forms underwent some minor changes until 1956, when improved forms were adopted for general reports. The *hsien* (county) was made the unit for reporting compiled data from the *hsiang* (township). These *hsien* reports, prepared by the *hsien* People's Councils, were the basis for the preparation of general reports by provinces, autonomous regions, and municipalities.

After 1954, a special statistical study was undertaken for determining the sown acreage by distributing forms to the *hsien,* with the responsibility for reporting delegated to mutual aid and cooperative organizations as well as to the *hsien* cadres.

The instructions for the computation of sown acreage, harvested acreage, multiple cropping, and types of yields appear adequate if followed and objectively collected.

Types of yields are explained as those compiled on the basis of sown acreage, harvested acreage, and cultivated acreage for each category.

The statistical study explains that for agricultural plan-

[6] Editorial Committee, *Handbook of Agricultural Statistical Work* (Peking: Statistical Publishing House, 1956), English translation, American Consulate General, Hong Kong, No. 434, Jan. 15, 1957.

ning and for the examination of plans, yields are computed
on the basis of sown acreage. In this connection, no indication is given whether the yield is based on reports of expected harvested yield or on actual harvested yield.

However, in a concluding paragraph on yields it states
that each crop is considered separately in computing yields.
The harvests of a crop are added together and divided by
sown acreage or harvested acreage. Two crops are used as an
example where total harvest of a crop grown on several *mow*
is divided by the number of *mow* to obtain harvested yield
per *mow*. The *Handbook* does not indicate how local organizations should obtain data upon which to base these
calculations.

After 1956, work was begun on the computation of yields
on the basis of cultivated acreage for the purpose of reflect-
ing progress in production per unit of land.

As to the reliability of Communist agricultural statistics,
there is sufficient reason to question the data because those
reporting are concerned with the fulfillment of quotas or
goals. The Peking government itself is interested in providing the public with data that indicate progress in order to
substantiate the political and economic objectives of its
regime. It is apparent, however, that no objective method
was devised for obtaining reasonably reliable data.

The confusion in statistical reporting, the subordination
of statistics in 1958 strictly to Communist party goals, and
the collection of the data by untrained party officers as well
as by the masses are aptly described by John S. Aird, with
full references to the Chinese sources in Chapter 5 of his
work on population.[7] A monograph by Dr. C. M. Li also
deals with Communist statistical methods.[8]

[7] John S. Aird, *The Size, Composition, and Growth of the Population of
Mainland China,* Bureau of Census, International Population Statistics Reports, Series p–90, No. 15 (Washington, D. C.: Government Printing Office,
1961).

[8] Choh-ming Li, *The Statistical System of Communist China* (Berkeley
and Los Angeles: University of California Press, 1962).

The irony of the situation is that the Communist food production data for 1949–58, instead of supporting party policies, contradict them—a contention that is fully substantiated in the succeeding analysis.

The Communist statistical data on land, crop hectares, and production in *The Great Ten Years,*[9] although apparently manipulated to indicate an increase in production, are used in this monograph to compare Communist claims with those of the pre-Communist period.

## III.  COMPARATIVE AMOUNTS OF CULTIVATED LAND

*The Relationship between the NARB Estimates and the LU Farm Survey for the Pre-Communist Period*

(See Table 1 and Appendix Tables 1, 2, and 3.) A basic difference between the *LU* Farm Survey data and the NARB Estimates is the figure for cultivated land. Unfortunately, the 65.8 million hectares (254,018 square miles) of cultivated land for 22 provinces, used by NARB for computing production, did not include unregistered land, popularly known as "black land," not paying taxes.

Actual land surveys under the Nationalists in the Yangtze Delta area for four *hsien* had revealed nearly one-fourth of the land as not registered. In Kiang-ning *hsien,* near Nanking, where land registration and land-tax collection were modernized, enough additional land was added to the tax records to reduce the tax rate for every land owner. In Kwan-hsien, Szechwan, a land survey indicated that one-half of the cultivated land was not registered.

The *LU* field enumerators were assigned the task of obtaining estimates from the local people on the amount of this unregistered land belonging to small as well as large owners. In the course of their investigations, they also dis-

[9] State Statistical Bureau, *Wei-ta ti Shih-nien* (The Great Ten Years) (Peking, 1959).

TABLE 1.* COMPARATIVE AMOUNTS OF CULTIVATED LAND, CROP HECTARES AND ANNUAL PRODUCTION OF FOOD GRAINS, POPULATION AND ANNUAL CONSUMPTION BY SOURCES OF DATA, MAINLAND CHINA. (FOR PRE-COMMUNIST PERIOD, 1929-37 AND COMMUNIST PERIOD, 1949-58)

Part I. Basic Data

| Sources of data | Cultivated land[1] (hectares) m | Crop hectares[2] m | Production of food grains[3] MMT | Available for food for total population of 592m (unprocessed) Total[4] MMT | Per capita[5] kgs | Available for farm population of 474m Total[6] MMT | Per farm capita[7] kgs | Remainder available for non-farm population of 118 Total[8] MMT | Per capita[9] kgs |
|---|---|---|---|---|---|---|---|---|---|
| I | II | III | IV | V | VI | VII | VIII | IX | X |
| Pre-Communist period *Statistical Monthly* | | | | | | | | | |
| 1929-37 | 77 | 80 | 137 | 117 | 198 | 129 | 273 | -12 | — |
| NARB Official-M 1931-37 | 80 | 89 | 131 | 112 | 189 | 136 | 286 | -24 | — |
| NARB Revised-M 1931-37 | 102 | 114 | 170 | 144 | 243 | 136 | 286 | 8 | 68 |
| Combined Estimates-M 1929-33 | 102 | 124 | 188 | 161 | 272 | 129 | 273 | 32 | 271 |
| LU Farm Survey-M 1929-33 | 102 | 111 | 182 | 156 | 262 | 129 | 273 | 27 | 228 |
| Communist period *The Great Ten Years* 1949-58 | 107 | 114 | 163 | 138ᵃ | 231ᵃ | 113ᵇ | 237ᵇ | 25ᵃ | 212ᵃ |

Part II. Comparison of Processed Food Grains and Calories Available from LU Farm Survey-M Production, 1929-33, and from Communist Claimed Production, 1949-58, for Total Population, Mainland China

| Sources of data | Daily grams of processed food grains per capita | Calories available daily per capita From food grains | Calories available daily per capita Estimated for all foods | Calories per capita from all food adjusted for food grains imported or exported |
|---|---|---|---|---|

| | I | II | III | IV | V |
|---|---|---|---|---|---|
| Pre-Communist period[10] *LU Farm Survey-M*, 1929–33 | | 575 | 2,023 | 2,365 | 2,410 |
| Communist period[11] *The Great Ten Years*, 1949–58 | | 509 | 1,776 | 2,078 | 2,017 |

Notes to Table 1.

* Throughout the tables in this book the following abbreviations are used: m=million; and MMT=million metric tons.

1 From Appendix Table 2.

2 From Appendix Table 4.

3 From Appendix Table 5.

4 Computed by factor of 85.5 per cent available for food as in col. III, Appendix Table 11.

5 Col. V divided by total population.

6 Col. VIII multiplied by farm population except for Communist which is from Appendix Table 12, col. VI.

7 The 273 kg for *Statistical Monthly* data is assumed to be the same as for *LU Farm Survey-M*. The 286 kg based on the NARB 1937 food survey for most usual consumption, for 22 provinces, Appendix Table 9, col. VI, is used for NARB Official-M and NARB Revised-M and is assumed to apply to mainland China, although, in *LU Survey-M* the addition of Manchuria, Sikang, and Sinkiang increased the per capita amount by 3 kg.

For Combined Estimates-M, the *LU Survey* of 273 kg is used. The 273 kg for *LU Survey-M* is from col. II, Part II A, Appendix Table 11, based on the *LU Survey* 1929-33, Appendix Table 9, col. III.

The 237 kg for Communist data is obtained by dividing 113 MMT in the previous column by farm population of 477.4 million, Appendix Table 12, col. II.

8 Col. V minus col. VII.

9 Col. IX divided by non-farm population.

10 Data are from Appendix Table 12, Part II Section C.

11 Data are from Appendix Table 12, Part II Section C.

a For Communist 1949-58 end-of-year average total population of 597 million.

b For Communist 1949-58 end-of-year average farm population of 477 million.

c For Communist 1949-58 end-of-year average nonfarm population 119 million. The Communist series of end-of-year population begins with 542 million in 1949 and increases each year to 658 million 1958 (5).

*Comment:* The *LU Farm Survey-M* population of 592 million for mainland China, Table 5, is used for all pre-Communist period sources. The Communist population is stated in notes 10, 11 and 12 to this table.

covered that the amount of cultivated land on the books of
the *hsien* governments was greater than that in the provincial
records, and that the amount given in the provincial records
was greater than that registered in the national government
records. According to the *LU* investigation for 148 *hsien*, the
average of all corrections by *hsien* of cultivated land indicates a total of 88 million hectares (339,644 square miles)
for the *LU* Eight Agricultural Areas (22 provinces), instead
of 65.8 million hectares, whereas the average of the highest
estimates in each *hsien* is 93.8 million hectares, or 362,082
square miles (see *LU*-A, p. 165, Table 3, items 1 and 2, and
Appendix Table 1). The figure of 88 million hectares was
adopted in the *LU* analysis because it is the better figure
statistically, although 93.8 million hectares for 22 provinces
may have been the more nearly correct figure as a result of
underestimates. Thus, the correction factor for the NARB
amount of cultivated land for 22 provinces is 133.7 per cent
(88 ÷ 65.8 x 100).

The total cultivated land for mainland China is obtained
by adding the figures for Manchuria, Sikang, and Sinkiang
of 14.4 million hectares (Appendix Table 3) to the 88 million hectares (Appendix Table 3) to the 88 million hectares
which makes a total of 102.4 million hectares of cultivated
land for both *LU* Farm Survey-M and NARB Revised-M as
well as for Combined Estimates.

This amount may be compared with a new official figure
of 93.2 million hectares of cultivated land for mainland
China published by the Directorate of Statistics in 1946 (see
Shen, *op. cit.*, p. 142). The method of arriving at this figure
is not explained in connection with the table which enumer-
ates cultivated land by mainland provinces and Taiwan.
Data for Taiwan are omitted to obtain the total of 93.2 million hectares, but it is still lower than the *LU* 102.4 million
hectares. However, the NARB computations for production
continued to be based on 65.8 million hectares for 22
provinces.

*Cultivated Land under the Communists Contrasted with Pre-Communist Period* (Table 1 and Appendix Table 2)

The Communist cultivated land data appear to be more objective and more reliable than the production data compiled by a different Communist agency. Communist reports indicate that a serious attempt was made to ascertain the amount of cultivated land, and it is probable that the land figure was subject to less manipulation than were the production data.

The 1949–58 average of 107 million hectares of cultivated land is almost the same as the 108 million hectares for the highest *LU* Farm Survey-M estimate of cultivated land. The Communists made a correction for the cultivated land figure used by NARB and began their 1949–58 series with a claim of 97.9 million hectares in 1949. Increases were recorded every year by the Communists up to 112 million hectares in 1956; thereafter, the claims decreased to 107.8 million hectares in 1958, which was slightly lower than the highest *LU* estimate of 108.2 million hectares (93.8 million for 22 provinces, plus 14.4 million for Manchuria, Sikang, and Sinkiang). The Communist data on cultivated land for the first few years appear to be primarily a statistical increase, but by 1953 the data may reflect, in part, an attempt to bring poorer lands into cultivation. The 107.8 million hectares for 1958 may be a deflation of the statistics, a decrease from former years due to unproductivity of new lands, mismanagement causing some land to lie idle, a directive to increase yields on a smaller area, or a combination of these factors.

## IV. COMPARATIVE AMOUNTS OF CROP HECTARES IN FOOD GRAIN CROPS BY SOURCE OF DATA

(See Table 1 and Appendix Table 4.) Because some land produces more than one crop per year, the term "crop

hectares," instead of "crop area," to denote area of all crops
sown, or harvested, is used. Thus, on such areas, crop hectares are greater than the number of hectares in cultivated
land. The data for the *LU* Farm Survey and the NARB
Estimates are for crops harvested, whereas the Communist
data are for crops sown. The specific crops included under
the term "food grains" are described in note (1) to Appendix Table 4.

The amount of crop hectares in food grains for a given
area depends not only on the amount of cultivated land but
also on the extent of multiple cropping, which is measured
by the index of multiple cropping of food grains—i.e., crop
hectares divided by hectares of cultivated land.

### Crop Hectares in Food Grains for the
### Pre-Communist Period

The total crop hectares given in the *Statistical Monthly*
and the NARB Estimates-M are gross underestimates because
of omission of unregistered cultivated land, as already explained, and, therefore, are not acceptable for interpretation
of Communist crop hectares.

The total crop hectares vary, in rounded quantities, from
111 million for the *LU* Survey-M to 114 million for the
NARB Estimates-M and 124 million for the Combined
Estimates-M, even though the amount of 102 million of
cultivated land is the same for the three sources. In terms of
the index of multiple cropping of food grains, the corresponding variation is 108, 112, and 121. The Combined
Estimates for the 22 provinces indicate more multiple
cropping in the Spring Wheat, Winter Wheat-Millet, and
Winter Wheat-Kaoliang Areas than in the *LU* Farm Survey.
The reason is not clear, but the acceptability of 124 million
hectares will be tested later under the topic of food consumption.

Significant differences also occur for crop hectares between sources of data by groups of crops (Appendix Table 4). For instance, the NARB Revised-M crop hectares have the following percentage differences from the *LU* Survey-M: rice, 84; wheat, 125; miscellaneous, 108; and potatoes, 79 per cent. For the Combined Estimates-M, there are similar differences compared with the *LU* Survey-M for rice and wheat, but for miscellaneous grains and potatoes the percentages are higher —126 and 101 per cent, respectively. Several factors may account for all or part of this variation. Crop hectare variation for rice may be caused in part by different interpretations, or uses, of the term "per cent of crop area." For instance, in areas where two separate crops of rice are grown the same year on the same land, they might be reported as one crop or double the amount.

A second factor is the interplanting of rice which might be reported as one crop or double this amount. Although planting dates and harvesting dates differ for early and late planted rice, only one unit of land is used because one half is in early rice and the other in late rice.

A third factor is the probable difference in the extent to which all minor crops were included in the various sources of data. For both NARB Estimates-M and *LU* Farm Survey-M, the food grains enumerated in the source data as individual crops other than rice, wheat, and potatoes (grain-equivalent) were classified as "miscellaneous" to correspond with the Communist classification. For instance, the NARB Estimates are designated as the "principal crops," which implies some food grains were not included, but the *LU* survey includes all food grain crops. There is no itemization for the Communist miscellaneous grains.

The Chinese cropping systems are very complex in that considerable areas of food grains are interplanted with crops such as corn and soybeans, corn and green beans, wheat and field peas, and many other combinations. One of the problems is to determine the proportion of a hectare occupied by two interplanted crops, and the yield of each. Cropping systems are recorded for 154 localities (see *LU-B,* Table 18, pp. 253–269).

A fourth factor might be the methods of compiling the raw data into final estimates.

A fifth possible factor is the relative extent of territory actually represented by the different sources correlated with the accuracy of the estimation method and compared with the actual enumeration. The basic data for the Combined Estimates and for the NARB Estimates of crop hectares for 22 provinces were computed from several thousand reporters' estimates of "per cent of crop area" in each crop. The *LU* Farm Survey data are based on hectares in each crop reported by farmers for their own land for 100 farms in each of 167 localities in 22 provinces. As described previously, an attempt was made to select localities to represent as large an area as possible.

These variations in crop hectare figures between different groups of crops are important because they affect the estimates of production—primarily because of large differences in yields of rice and potatoes per unit of land. Such production, when cross-checked with reported farm food consumption, as will be described later, should be an aid in determining which amount of crop hectares for each of the four groups of crops may be the more acceptable.

### Crop Hectares in Food Grain in the Communist Period
(Table 1 and Appendix, Table 4).

The 1949–58 Communist average of 114 million crop hectares is the same as for NARB Revised-M and indicates no increase in multiple cropping of food grains for the Communist period. A more accurate comparison is the index of multiple cropping of 106 for the Communist period compared with 112 for the NARB Estimates-M, 121 for Combined Estimates-M, and 108 for the *LU* Survey-M.

It was only in 1956 and 1958 that the Communist index of multiple cropping exceeded 108 for *LU* Survey-M and only in 1958—a year of greatly exaggerated data—that it equalled 112 ~~million~~ for NARB Revised-M; but, in no year did it reach 121 for the Combined Estimates-M.

It is clear that, according to Communist statistics, the index of multiple cropping was below that of the pre-Communist period. This difference may be caused in part by the higher amounts of cultivated land recorded for the Communist than for the pre-Communist period.

## V. THE RELATIONSHIP BETWEEN FOOD GRAIN PRODUCTION AND SOURCES OF DATA

(See Table 1 and Appendix Table 5.) The total production of 170 million metric tons for the NARB Revised-M is 93 per cent of 182 million metric tons for the *LU* Survey-M. There are two reasons for this lower production: (1) the 26.8 million crop hectares in rice are considerably less than the 31.9 million for the *LU* Survey-M (Appendix Table 4); and (2) the average yield of rice for 22 provinces, 2,534 kilograms per hectare for the NARB Estimates, is significantly less than the most frequent median yield of 2,775 kilograms for the *LU* Farm Survey. The high production of 188 million metric tons for the Combined Estimates-M is due to the same reasons plus a higher amount of crop hectares in miscellaneous grains. For a further discussion of yields, see Section VI.

*Communist Production of Food Grains Compared with the Pre-Communist Period* (Table 1 and Appendix Table 5)

Although the Communist 1949–58 annual series of production data appear to indicate significant increases, they are misleading.

The Communist 1949–58 average production of 163 million metric tons is 96 per cent of 170 million metric tons for the NARB Estimates-M, 90 per cent of 182 million metric tons for the *LU* Survey-M, and 86 per cent of the Combined Estimates-M (Table 1).

The Communist annual series of production begins with a claimed production of 108 million metric tons in 1949, a year with below average yield. O. L. Dawson, former Agricultural Attaché of the U. S. Department of Agriculture (USDA), estimated it at 12 per cent below average. If the Communist reduction was based on the NARB Estimates-M for mainland China of 131 million metric tons for 1931–37, the percentage reduction would be about 18 per cent.

An extremely important observation on the compilations for 1949 is that, while cultivated land was increased to 97.9 million hectares compared with NARB Estimates-M of 80.2 million hectares, a corresponding adjustment was not made in production for each of the four groups of food grains. If the NARB Estimates-M are taken as 100, the index of change for Communist 1949 data is as follows: cultivated land, 123; total production, 83; rice crop hectares, 128 and unhulled rice production, 96; wheat crop hectares, 98 and wheat production, 59; miscellaneous crop hectares, 111 and miscellaneous production, 71; potato crop hectares, 189 and potato production (grain equivalent), 141.

Thus, the initial figure in 1949 for Communist production is in serious error and invalidates the yearly increases. Apparently, statistical adjustments were made over a period of years—possibly as late as 1956. The 1958 claimed production of 250 MMT is exaggerated, as will be discussed later.

Even by 1957, claimed production was only 185 million metric tons, or an increase of 9.4 per cent above the NARB Revised-M of 170 million metric tons, only 2 per cent more than the *LU* Farm Survey-M of 182 million metric tons, but two per cent less than the Combined Estimates production of 189 million metric tons.

The 1949–58 average amount of Communist production for each group of food grains contrasts significantly with both the NARB Revised-M 1931–37 production figure and the *LU* Farm Survey-M figure for 1929–33. In rounded quantities and in the above order, the amounts in metric tons are as follows: rice 74, 68, and 88; wheat 21, 31, and 24; miscellaneous 50, 63, and 58; potatoes 19, 9 and 11. Thus, the amount of rice production by the Communists falls between the amounts of the other two food grain sources; wheat and miscellaneous grain production are lowest; and potatoes, the highest.

For wheat, both crop hectares and production are low. Wheat yields, as shown in Appendix Table 6, are also significantly less than in both the NARB Estimates-M and in the *LU* Farm Survey-M. The reasons for this change in wheat yields should, if possible, be clarified. Improved varieties of wheat made available by plant breeders before the advent of the Communist regime would lead one to expect an increase in wheat production—especially since wheat is one of the principal grains.[10] In no year did the Chinese Communist wheat production reach the NARB Revised-M amount of 30.6 million metric tons for 1931–37, and only in 1956 and 1958 did their claims exceed the *LU* Farm Survey-M average of 24.2 million metric tons.

For miscellaneous grains, as for wheat, both crop hectares and production are low compared with NARB Estimates-M and *LU* Farm Survey-M, because of fewer crop hectares and lower reported yields. A possible explanation for the lower yields may be the Communist government's emphasis on

[10] Harry Houser Love and John Henry Reisner, *The Cornell-Nanking Story*, the First International Technical Cooperation Program in Agriculture by Cornell University, Department of Plant Breeding, New York State College of Agriculture (Ithaca, N. Y.: Cornell University, 1963).

the principal grains, although the above record for wheat
does not support this contention. Perhaps, with less official
attention to miscellaneous grains, production would be
under-reported with little chance of discovery.

It is reasonable to assume that the emphasis on production
of potatoes did cause increases in their production because
potatoes could be fitted into the rotation system easily.
Nevertheless, 45 million metric tons in potato grain-equivalent in 1958, double that of 1957, appears to be an exaggeration, as are the figures for other crops, except possibly
wheat.

One may conclude these observations on Communist production with the statement that the Communists have un-
wittingly recorded their 1949–58 production as lower than
that of both 1929–33 and 1931–37.

## VI. YIELDS IN RELATION TO PRODUCTION

Before discussing differences in yields between sources of
data, we must consider different usage of the term "yield."

Yields for all pre-Communist sources for 22 provinces are
harvested yields per crop hectare. The yields reported in the
*Statistical Monthly* are the most frequent ones obtained by
farmers. The NARB Estimates are the average yields for
the period 1931–37. The *LU* Farm Survey yields are of two
types reported by farmers for the land they farmed. One is
the "most frequent yields" for a period of ten years prior
to the year of study of 100 farms in each locality over the
period, 1919–33 (see *LU-B,* Table 9, pp. 209–210 and Table
14, pp. 223–26). The other type is the average yields for
different years of study during the period of 1929–33; they
are not an average over a long period.

All the yields for pre-Communist sources are the amount
of harvest the farmers reported as after threshing at the

farmstead, or sometimes—as in the case of rice—as "after threshing in boxes in the field."

The Communist yields derived from *The Great Ten Years* are production divided by acreage sown. Directions to local officials state that yields are the amount harvested divided by crop hectares sown or harvested. Thus, actual yields might vary, depending on whether sown or harvested acreage was used in the computations.

### Contrasts in Yield by Sources of Data for 22 Provinces in the Pre-Communist Period

In the previous discussion on production of food grains, reference was made to the significant difference in the rice yield for 22 provinces—namely, 2,534 kilograms for the NARB Estimates and the median of most frequent yields of 2,775 kilograms for the *LU* Farm Survey.

Although there is this considerable variation between the two sources in yields of rice, there is very close agreement for yields of wheat, miscellaneous grains, and potatoes for 22 provinces. These yields in kilograms for NARB Estimates are 1,079, 1,135, and 1,933 kilograms compared with corresponding *LU* Farm Survey figures of 1,067, 1,134, and 1,936 kilograms.

The *LU* Farm Survey rice yield is the median of all "most frequent yields" for all types of rice arranged in a frequency distribution (Appendix Table 7). These types of rice include the main rice crop (on land growing only one rice crop during the year); glutinous rice; interplanted rice (combined yields of early planted rice in widely spaced rows and a later planting between these rows are considered as yield per one crop hectare); double cropping of rice (an early crop of rice which, after harvest, is followed by a late crop of rice). The harvest of early rice is considered as yield per one crop-hectare and the harvest of the late crop, as yield per one crop-hectare.

The median of the most frequent rice yields is used instead of the average of most frequent yields to eliminate any possible bias of a few very high yields. The average of the *LU* Farm Survey most frequent yields (see *LU-B,* Table 14 pp. 222–23) for all types of rice is 2,972 kg when weighted by per cent of crop hectares (see *LU-B,* Appendix Table 2, p. 174) in each type of rice.

Some of the reasons for differences between the rice yield of 2,534 kilograms for the NARB Estimates and the *LU* Farm Survey median most frequent yield of 2,775 kilograms may be similar to those for crop hectares explained under the topic "crop hectares."

Also, for example, the NARB Estimates for Kwangtung and Kwangsi provinces (see Appendix Table 2 in "Agricultural Resources" [Shen, *op. cit.*]) indicates a rice yield of 2,559 kilograms per hectare when production is divided by crop hectares. The *LU* Farm Survey yield for the Double Cropping Area, which includes chiefly Kwangtung and Kwangsi, is 2,025 kilograms for all types of rice—early and late, main crop, glutinous, and irrigated as well as non-irrigated. The yield of 2,559 kilograms is too high for either early or late rice, but too low for the combined yields of both crops. If the production figure is divided by the *LU* Farm Survey yield of 2,025 kilograms, the crop hectares are increased by 1 million crop hectares, or 1.3 million when multiplied by the land correction factor of 133.7 per cent. Apparently, some NARB reporters disregarded the fact that, while the land producing rice was one hectare of land, the two distinct crops of early and late rice are two crop hectares. Although this does not account for all of the discrepancy in the respective yields of 2,534 kilograms and 2,752 kilograms, it is one of the factors.

In spite of all attempts, the reasons for the discrepancy in crop hectares and yields of rice between NARB Estimates and *LU* Farm Surveys figures have not been discovered. Later, the discussion on consumption may indicate which yield figure, as it affects production, appears more probable.

*Comparison of Yields for Mainland China by Sources of Data for the Pre-Communist Period* (Appendix Table 6)

The significant differences in yields of all food grains per crop hectare for mainland China are due chiefly to variation in yields of rice. However, the potato yield given in the *Statistical Monthly* is less than that cited in other sources, while the yield of miscellaneous grains is listed as higher. The reasons for this are not clear, although faulty data may be the cause.

*Comparison of Communist Yields with the Pre-Communist Period for Mainland China* (Appendix Table 6)

The Communist average yield for 1949–58 of 1,430 kilograms is about the same as the average for the NARB Revised-M but is significantly less than the yield for the *LU* Survey-M, particularly because of much lower yields for rice and lower ones for wheat and miscellaneous grains.

The 1949–58 year-to-year variation in yield figures for each group of grain crops appears to be partly due to recording crop hectares and production at different rates of yearly increase. This is particularly evident for rice with significant variations, higher or lower, each year.

*Variation in Yields Caused by Growing Conditions*
(Tables 2 and 3)

The interpretation of yields as they affect production is facilitated by an understanding of variation in yields caused by growing conditions independent of other factors.

TABLE 2. VARIATION IN *LU* FARM SURVEY CROP YIELDS PER CROP
HECTARE CAUSED BY GROWING CONDITIONS (16,333 FARMS, 162
LOCALITIES, 150 *Hsien*, 22 PROVINCES CHINA, 1929–33)[1]

| Types of yields | Percent variation with most frequent yields as 100 | Harvested yields per crop hectare kg | Percent variation with normal as 100 |
|---|---|---|---|
| I | II | III | IV |
| Average[2] | 99.1 | 1,671 | 78.41 |
| Most frequent[3] | 100.0 | 1,686 | 79.12 |
| Normal[4] | 126.4 | 2,131 | 100.00 |
| Best[4] | 144.0 | 2,428 | 113.94 |

[1] Reference, pp. 222-23, Table 3 (2) and p. 208, Table 8 (3) for percentage variation in yields compared with more frequent yields taken as 100. The percentages in col. 2 of this table have been converted in terms of normal yields as 100 (col. 4) for each of comparing types of yields, since normal is usually considered as 100.

[2] The *LU* Farm Survey average yields in Table 3, p. 223 (2) are in rounded percentages of most frequent yields while in Table 8, p. 208 (3) percentages are carried to one-tenth of one per cent. For this study percentages in Table 8, p. 208 (3) for each *LU* Agricultural Area have been weighted by crop hectares in each Area. This procedure indicates that the *LU* Farm Survey average yields are 99.1 per cent of *LU* most frequent yields rather than 98.1 per cent when weighted by localities as in Table 8. For the Wheat Region the percentage is 98.4 and for the Rice Region 99.6.

Thus, the average yields of crops for the years of study in each locality are in close relationship with the most frequent yields. Since most frequent yields are usually very near average yields for a period of ten years or more they may be considered as an average yield.

[3] The most frequent yields for the *LU* Farm Survey are for crops grown on 20 per cent or more farms in each locality, pp. 209-10, Table 9. They are for a ten year period previous to the year of study during 1929-33.

[4] Normal and best yields ever obtained are for the period in the experience of each 100 farmers in each locality. Such yields cannot be expected for an entire country in any one year.

In every country, yields per unit of land vary with growing conditions for crops. These differences have been referred to by Buck (*LU-A*, pp. 222–23) and also in a USDA publication.[11] Types of yields linked to growing conditions are "average," "most frequent," "normal," and "best yields" (Table 2).

Average yields, in order to be representative, should cover a ten-year period or longer.

Most frequent yields are about the same as average yields for a long period.

[11] United States Department of Agriculture, Bureau of Agricultural Economics, *The Agricultural Estimating and Reporting Services of the United States Department of Agriculture*, Misc. Pub., No. 703 (Washington, D. C.: Dec. 1949).

Normal yields are obtained when all growing conditions are favorable. Such yields seldom, if ever, occur over the entire area of a large country in the same year.

Best yields ever obtained occur when all growing conditions are exceptionally good. They cannot be expected for an entire large country in any one year.

These types of yields can be illustrated from common usage by Chinese farmers who refer to them in terms of "parts," 10 parts being 100 per cent. A normal yield is *"shih-fen,"* 10 parts; extraordinary or best yields are denoted as *"shih-er-fen,"* or 12 parts. An average, or most frequent yield, is spoken of as *"ba-fen,"* or 8 parts.

The *LU* Farm Survey yields in 22 provinces for all crops vary from an average of 1,671 kilograms per crop hectare to 2,428 kilograms for the "best yields ever obtained" in the memory of the farmers (Table 2). The *LU* Farm Survey "most frequent yields" of 1,686 kilograms during the ten years prior to the date of obtaining the information is very close to the *LU* Farm Survey "average yield" of 1,671 kilograms per crop hectare for the period 1929–33. Since "most frequent yields" for a long period are about the same as "average yields" for a long period, the years of the *LU* study appear to have been about average years for crop production.

Thus, with ratios established for these yield variations in Table 2, column IV, providing one type of yield is known from other sources of adequate data, the various types of yields can be estimated. Such computations for mainland China are presented in Table 3. Reference to application of these ratios to other yield data is made on 222 of *LU-A*. These ratios are similar to those calculated in an early USDA publication for the United States (the exact reference to which is not available) and in the previously cited USDA publication.[12]

The Communist-claimed 1958 yield for mainland China

[12] *Ibid.*

of 2,061 kilograms per crop hectare is 295 kilograms higher than the NARB Estimates-M "good yield" of 1,766 kilograms for 1936—162 kilograms higher than the NARB "normal yield" of 1,899 kilograms but 33 kilograms lower than the *LU* "normal yield" of 2,094 kilograms per crop hectare. Even the NARB "good yield" falls short of the NARB "normal" by 123 kilograms.

If the Communist yield was also 123 kilograms short of the Communist "normal" of 1,824 kilograms, the yield for 1958 would be 1,701 instead of 2,061 kilograms per crop hectare, and the production would be 206 million metric tons for 121.3 million crop hectares instead of 250 million metric tons. Moreover, if 121.3 million crop hectares for

TABLE 3. VARIATIONS IN YIELDS CAUSED BY GROWING CONDITIONS IN 22 PROVINCES APPLIED TO YIELDS FOR MAINLAND CHINA

| | Yields by types computed from percentage variations | | | | |
|---|---|---|---|---|---|
| Sources of data | Average[1] kg | Normal[2] kg | Best[3] kg | Yield in an exceptional year kg | year |
| I | II | III | IV | V | VI |
| *Pre-Communist period* | | | | | |
| *LU* Farm Survey-M, 1929–33 | 1,642 | 2,094 | 2,386 | — | — |
| NARB Revised-M, 1931–37 | 1,489 | 1,899 | 2,164 | 1,776[a] | 1936 |
| Combined Estimates-M, 1929–33 | 1,522 | 1,942 | 2,214 | — | — |
| *Communist period* | | | | | |
| The Great Ten Years, 1949–58 | 1,430 | 1,824 | 2,078 | 2,061[b] | 1958 |

[1] Average yields for mainland China are from Appendix Table 6.

[2] Normal yields are computed by dividing the average yields by 78.41 per cent, line one, col. IV, Table 2.

[3] Best yields are obtained by multiplying the normal yield (obtained by method in note 2 above) by 113.94 per cent, line 4, col. IV, Table 2.

[a] The NARB Estimates for 1936 production is 138.7 MMT for 22 provinces which is a 19.5 per cent increase over NARB Estimates 1931-37 average production of 116.1 MMT. The average production for Manchuria, Sikang and Sinkiang is 14.9 MMT which, increased by 19.5 per cent, indicates a production of 17.8 MMT for 1936. The NARB Estimates for production of 138.7 MMT multiplied by the cultivated land correction factor of 1.337 indicates a production of 185.4 MMT for 1936 for the 22 provinces. Thus, 185.4 MMT plus 17.8 MMT for Manchuria, Sikang and Sinkiang portray a mainland production in 1936 of 200.3 MMT. This divided by NARB Estimates-M of 114.4 million crop hectares, Appendix Table 4, portrays a yield of 1,776 kg per crop hectare for the good year of 1936 for mainland China.

[b] Claimed production of 250 MMT divided by claimed crop hectares of 121.3 million.

1958 is an exaggeration like other 1958 data, then—in view of the fact that an increase in multiple cropping was one of the goals and the number of crop hectares may have been inflated—the crop hectares may have been only 116.9 million obtained by computing crop hectares at the same rate of decline from 1957 as reported for cultivated land. Thus, if the yield were 1,701 kilograms, i.e., 123 kilograms less than the Communist "normal yield," the production would be 199 million metric tons instead of 250. Even such a yield for 1958 has doubtful validity as will be discussed further in the next section under "A Possible Revision of the Exaggerated 1958 Production Figure."

## VII. VALIDITY OF THE COMMUNIST 1949–58 PRODUCTION OF 163 MILLION METRIC TONS AND OF THE 1958 CLAIMED PRODUCTION OF 250 MILLION METRIC TONS

### Production in 1949–58

Since the Communist series of data on food grains production is erroneous as a series, one may well question the validity of the average 163 MMT of the 1949–58 series as representative of the actual production.

First, there is no logical reason for assuming that production did increase year by year, even when Communist data indicate an annual increase of population. The initial figure for Communist production in 1949 is in serious error—even allowing for a poor crop year caused by unfavorable growing conditions—and invalidates the apparent yearly increases.

Precise information on the extent to which production was adversely affected from approaching usual production in the years 1950 and 1951 is not available. If transportation was inadequate to market products to the cities, it could affect the production of these products. The chief check on this point would be whether there was a shortage of such products in the cities. My own observation from many years in China is that farmers continue to produce in spite of political and military upheavals, and that the areas seriously affected are small in relation to the total although the implementation of the violent land redistribution program during 1950–52 may have been more disruptive.

In any attempt to adjust yearly Communist official data on food grain output, attention should be given to both the favorable and unfavorable factors affecting production.

Communist reports on technological advances emphasize tremendous accomplishments. On the other hand, there are numerous nonofficial reports from Communist sources not only on the failure of these efforts to increase production but even on their having adverse, rather than favorable, effects on production.

One of the sources (in English) on the unfavorable factors is the Union Research Institute publication.[13] Many of the unfavorable factors are corroborated by various sources, but limitation of time does not permit further elaboration in this monograph. A research project on the effect of these factors on production correlated with dates in relation to government implementation and in relation to weather should be a worthy contribution to an understanding of the effect of efforts to convert farming to a collective form of organization.

## *Factors Possibly Favoring Production*

### INHERITANCE OF AGRICULTURAL ADVANCES FROM THE PREVIOUS REGIME

These include established institutions for agricultural edu-

[13] *Communist China, 1949–59*, Vol. II (Kowloon, Hongkong: Union Research Institute). This publication contains 68 pages of discussion and data on grain purchase, requisition, and consumption. The consumption data are primarily for various years 1953 to 1957 and include reports and surveys of actual consumption.

cation, research, and extension; private and government banks lending credit to farmers' cooperatives; farmers' associations promoting improved methods; well-trained men; improved seeds such as wheat, rice, corn, soybeans, and cotton; methods of disease and insect control (see Love and Reisner, *op. cit.*) including control of virus in potatoes; land reform laws giving provinces the power to transfer land to farmers, an example being a very successful project near Chungking; a modern fertilizer factory in production near Nanking; mechanization of rice irrigation with Diesel engines in the Yangtze Delta area; a large scale Hwai River and Hungtze Lake water control project in construction, and blueprints of other water control projects. Thus, at the time of the Communist takeover, there was a good foundation for increasing production rather rapidly.

ADOPTION OF IMPROVED FARM PRACTICES.

1. Planting improved varieties and strains of crops. The extent of distribution of improved seed is dependent upon establishment of improved seed-production farms operated by government or through contract with farmers, or by seedsmen. By 1936, the University of Nanking was testing contracts with farmers. The extent to which the Communists solved this problem in an effective way is questionable, and there may be little or no information available.

2. Control of insects and diseases. There are Communist reports on manufacture of sprayers and production of insecticides and fungicides, but the quantities produced were comparatively small for the entire country.

3. Improved use of water for irrigation. This practice for existing small irrigation systems may have been effective, except for possible mismanagement of the systems.

4. Use of more fertilizers, particularly chemical ones. The increase in manufacture and imports of fertilizer was small compared with the need. Definite information on the propor-

tion applied to industrial crops like cotton and to food grains is not available.

5. Better rotation of crops, including more double cropping. There is no clear evidence that attempts in this direction were successful, except for potatoes, which could easily be adopted into the rotation systems. A successful increase in double cropping is dependent upon more fertilization.

6. Use of improved implements or machinery. The only successful examples are sprayers, pumps, and motors, although large machinery was introduced on state farms comprising a small acreage compared with the total for mainland China.

The extent of increase in production by adoption of these individual practices depends upon using a number of them simultaneously, such as: improved seeds with use of more fertilizer and a sufficient water supply; increased irrigation with the use of more fertilizers and improved seeds; and use of fertilizers with better seeds and adequate water supply. The extent to which these combined practices were used may have been limited.

### Factors Possibly Unfavorable to Production

*Weather.* There were good and bad years, probably about average for 1949–58.

*Pests and crop diseases.* Probably none of these were of very unusual magnitude during 1949–58.

*Incorrect farm practices.* Ill-advised farm practices, or good farm practices used in the wrong way or the wrong place—such as too deep plowing—may have been adopted as well as some of the following faulty practices:

1. Extension of new crop varieties without sufficient testing for their adaption to soil and climate conditions.
2. Too close spacing of plants and too thick sowing of seed.

3. Obedience to ill-advised directives from Peking on what, how, and when to plant.

4. Change in types of crops to be grown without regard to rotations adapted to soil, climate, and use of crops for food, feed, fodder, seed, and in industry. The increase in area planted to potatoes was a good practice, but the attempt to increase area in rice may have resulted in displacing other more profitable crops. In general, rice growing in China was formerly extended too far up on hill lands where water supply was not dependable—farmers in Szechwan call it "gambling with heaven." Some of these farmers discontinued rice on these hill lands in favor of corn and soybeans which gave greater production.

5. Irrigation of land without sufficient drainage to prevent salinity and waterlogging.

6. "Decreasing area" and "increasing yield," resulting in lower production.

7. Improper care and feeding of labor animals, including lack of training of young animals for work, with resultant shortage of animal power and the necessity for people to pull plows.

8. Neglect of small implements and their repair, and reduction of their manufacture. Part of the situation may have been caused by emphasis on semi-mechanized equipment or new but unadapted implements such as the new plows; thus there was a shortage of implements.

9. Shifting emphasis first to extensive farming, then to intensive or smaller acreage, and then a return to earlier methods.

REORGANIZATION OF THE FARM PRODUCTION UNIT

1. The methods used in the initial land reform have been reported to have discouraged production in terms of economic size. Absence of government services to new owners to replace services rendered by former landlords may also have resulted in decreased production.

2. The reorganization of farms into progressively larger units, and ultimately into communes, affected production adversely in the following way:

(a) The farmer's incentive progressively decreased with each larger unit.[14]

(b) Communist reports have stated that about one half of the cooperative joint farming units were not as efficient as individual farms.

(c) Mismanagement by a committee, or by inexperienced managers.

(d) At best, in a diversified agriculture, such as in most of China, efficient large-scale operation is difficult, if not impossible, because of the necessity of adapting farm operations to daily weather changes, to varying types of soil conditions, and to efficient cropping systems adapted to different soils.

(e) Inefficient use of labor in gangs.

(f) Possible depletion of labor supply on farms for work on massive projects. This is especially true if it occurred during peak periods of farm work such as plowing, planting, cultivating, and harvesting.

(g) The many Communist mandates sending or urging people back to the land to increase agricultural production is a sign of an unhealthy agriculture. If there had been progress in agriculture, the movement of population should have been toward the cities into professional and service occupations.

The extent to which reasonable numerical quantities of production can be assigned to each of these favorable and unfavorable factors is problematical. These factors, however, should receive careful consideration in any revision of Communist production data. They may be deserving of a special research effort. Otherwise, estimating the annual production for each year, 1949–58, without more specific information on favorable and unfavorable factors, leads to estimates which may, or may not, represent the true production. Possibly, the average 1949–58 production might have been somewhat

[14] Charles Hoffman, "Work Incentives in Communist China," Reprint No. 2 from *Industrial Relations*, Vol. III, No. 2, Feb., 1964 (Committee on Economy of China, Social Science Research Council [Berkeley: University of California]).

higher than the 163 million metric tons. Or, possibly, the yearly series would indicate a downward rather than an upward trend. The former Agricultural Attaché of the USDA, Mr. Dawson, estimates the 1949–58 production at 173 million metric tons. The average of Dr. Y. L. Wu's year-by-year estimates in Table 3 of his monograph, which follows, is 181 million metric tons for 1950–58 and 178 million metric tons for 1950–59.

A check on the average of 163 million metric tons is computed from Dr. Wu's quoted and estimated rations for 1950–59 as given in Table 1, note for column 9 of his monograph. The computations are as follows: The average of annual rations for 1950–59 is 238 kilograms of processed grain per adult. The 238 kilograms divided by 1.3 (the persons per adult-male unit in the *LU* Food Survey) equals 183 kilograms per capita processed which, when divided by the processing factor of 0.801, gives 228 kilograms of unprocessed grain per capita.

This, multiplied by the average 1950–59 midyear population of 591 million, suggests a production of 134.7 MMT for food consumption. This amount divided by the factor of 85.5 per cent of total production for food equals 157.5 MMT. If the 1950–59 averages of 0.9 MMT for exports and 3.3 MMT for stocks are added, the required production to meet claimed utilization would be 162 MMT, compared with the Communist claimed production of 163 MMT for the same period. The validity of this comparison depends primarily upon how nearly the rations used in the computation represent actual food consumption.

### A Possible Revision of the Exaggerated 1958 Production Figure

An inspection of the ten tests for the validity of the 1958 production of 250 million metric tons enumerated in Table 4 suggests consideration of item 6 (c) of 174 million metric

TABLE 4. VARIOUS TESTS OF RELIABILITY OF COMMUNIST CLAIMED PRODUCTION OF 250 MILLION METRIC TONS OF FOOD GRAINS IN 1958, MAINLAND CHINA

| Items | Production (MMT) |
|---|---|
| 1. Communist claim for 1958 with yield of 2,061 kg per crop hectare—a claim even greater than the normal yield of 1,899 kg for NARB and the good 1936 yield of 1,776 kg for NARB | 250 |
| 2. Reduction of 121.3 million crop hectares to 116.9 million, the same proportion as cultivated land declined from 111.8 million in 1957 to 107.8 million in 1958 | 241 |
| 3. Reduction on assumption that the yield of 2,061 kg was actually computed per hectare of cultivated land (107.8 million hectares in cultivated land multiplied by 2,061 kg) | 222 |
| 4. O. L. Dawson's judgment estimate | 210 |
| 5. Applying NARB good yield of 1,776 kg per crop hectare in 1936: | |
|     a) for claimed crop hectares of 121.3 million | 215 |
|     b) for reduced crop hectares of 116.9 million | 208 |
| 6. Applying a yield of 1,701 kg, the Communist normal yield of 1,824 kg minus 123 kg, to correspond with difference between NARB normal yield of 1,899 kg and the NARB good yield of 1,776 kg in 1936: | |
|     a) for claimed crop hectares of 121.3 million | 206 |
|     b) for reduced crop hectares of 116.9 million | 199 |
|     c) item 6b reduced by assumed 12.5 per cent for (1) loss of incentive and mismanagement in Agricultural Producers' Cooperatives and in Communes, and (2) for losses caused by ill-advised directives from Peking on what and how to plant. This reduction assumes that any increase from improved practices adopted is included in items (a) and (b) | 174 |
| 7. American Consulate, Hongkong | 192 |
| 8. Assuming Communist average yield of 1,430 kg per crop hectare (1949–58) were attained in 1958: | |
|     a) for claimed crop hectares of 121.3 million | 173 |
|     b) for claimed crop hectares of 116.9 million | 167 |
| 9. Dr. Y. L. Wu's estimate in his Table 3 | 175 |
| 10. Required production in 1958 to meet Communist reported utilization in 1956 and 1957[1] | |
|     a) Method 1, based on 1956 food consumption studies | 175 |
|     b) Method 2, based on 1956 food consumption studies | 161 |
|     c) Method 3, based on 1957 ration quoted by Dr. Y. L. Wu | 163 |

[1] Reports and surveys for 1956 indicate an average annual food grain consumption of 365 *catties* for the provinces of Hopei, Shangtung, Shansi and Honan and 483 *catties* for Liaoning province (24). Since the term "grain" is not defined in terms of amount of processing it may be assumed that the grain is unprocessed. On the other hand, the difference in consumption between the four provinces and Liaoning is so great that the 365 *catties* may be for processed grain. If unprocessed the 365 *catties* would be 182.5 kg per capita and the 483 *catties* would be 241.5 kg per capita. The former appears too low while the latter appears more reasonable, although it may be somewhat too high for 1956 compared with *LU* Farm Survey-M of 262 kg unprocessed grain per capita for total population. Therefore, three computations are made, the first, method 1, assumes that the 365 *catties* is processed grain and the 483 *catties* are unprocessed. The second method assumes that both amounts are unprocessed. A third method compares

tons, item 8 (a) of 173 million metric tons, and item 9 of 175 million metric tons as indicating the most probable production in 1958.

Item 5 (a) and 5 (b) and 6 (a) and 6 (b) in Table 4 are

---

the required production obtained in method two with 210 kg processed per adult for 1957 used by Dr. Y. L. Wu in his note 9, Table 1.

*Method 1.* The 365 *catties* is assumed to be processed grain and is converted to unprocessed grain by the factor of 0.861 for North China food grains which gives 424 *catties*, or 212 kg per capita. When 212.5 kg is given the weight of four for the four provinces and the 241.5 kg for Liaoning is given the weight of one, the average is 218 kg of unprocessed grain per capita.

A table on actual consumption in 1956 of "fine grain" in ten South China cities gives an average of 26.1 *catties* per month per capita, or 218 kg per capita per year unprocessed if a factor of 0.72 is used for milling unhulled rice. Since the consumption per capita is the same as 218 kg for North China the 218 kg may be considered as the possible average for the mainland in 1956.

It is suggested that the 1956 consumption of 218 kg of unprocessed food grains may be about the same as for 1958 because Communist claimed production for 1957 is only 5.7 per cent higher than in 1955 compared with the Communist increase in population of 4.8 per cent. Since there is reason to believe that the 1957 production was actually as low or lower than in 1956, one may disregard the apparent greater proportional increase in production. Thus, 218 kg per capita consumption in 1958 indicates 142 MMT available for food for the 1958 mid-year of 652.2 million population at 85.5 per cent of production available for food the production would be 166 MMT. According to Dr. Wu's Table 1, exports for 1958 were 1.2 MMT and the increase in stocks was 7.4 MMT, suggesting a required production of 175 MMT in 1958.

*Method 2.* However, if the annual food grain consumption of 365 *catties* per capita for the four provinces of Hopei, Shantung, Shansi, and Honan and the 483 *catties* for Liaoning are both considered as unprocessed grain then the weighted average of these provinces for North China of 194 kg weighted by 80 per cent for rural population and the ten cities average of 218 kg for non-farm population weighted by 20, the average would be 199 kg unprocessed grain per capita.

Because claimed production and population increased at about the same rate from 1955 to 1957 this apparent average of 199 kg unprocessed per capita in 1956 may be assumed as the consumption for 1958. The 199 kg multiplied by 652.2 million, the mid-year 1958 population, equals 129.9 MMT which divided by 85.5 per cent available for food equals 151.9 MMT. This plus 8.6 MMT for stocks and net exports per Dr. Y. L. Wu's Table 1 indicates a required production of 161 MMT to meet reported utilization.

*Method 3.* The 199 kg for capita in above method 2 are nearly the same amount as the ration for 1957 quoted by Dr. Y. L. Wu in his Table 1, note to col. 9, of 210 kg processed per adult when the latter is converted to a per capita basis according to the following computations: 210 divided by 1.3 (the persons per adult-male unit in the *LU* Food Survey) equals 161.5 kg per capita unprocessed. This divided by 0.801 for processing equals 202 kg per capita unprocessed. Since claimed production in 1957 was not substantially greater than in 1956, and probably was less, the 202 kg unprocessed per capita may be assumed as the possible consumption in 1958 from 1957 production. Thus, the mid-year population of 652.2 million multiplied by 202 kg gives a consumption of 131.7 MMT unprocessed food grains. This divided by the factor of 0.855 as available for food equals 154.2 MMT. If exports and stocks for 1958 of 8.6 MMT are included, the required production would be 163 MMT.

The 175 MMT required production for 1958 corresponds closely with item 6(c) of 174 MMT, with item 8 of 173 MMT and with item 9 of 175 MMT. Apparently the production in 1958 was no greater than 175 MMT but it may have been less according to the two computations 10(b) and 10(c) of 161 and 163 MMT. In conclusion, it is probable that more data exist on food utilization than presented here but the method used to estimate required production from utilization data may be of interest. There are estimates on food utilization based on Communist claimed production but they cannot represent actual utilization.

based solely on the assumption that growing conditions were so favorable that an almost normal yield could be expected. One may raise a query as to availability of sufficient information to justify this assumption.

Item 6 (c) in Table 4 assumes that the production was 10 to 15 per cent less that it would have been if farming had not been mismanaged. The figure of 12.5 per cent has been adopted to discount yields based on unfavorable factors other than weather conditions.

Item 10 based on utilization data, shows a variation from 161 to 175 in MMT. The estimates, (b) and (c), are close—161 and 163 MMT. The average of the three estimates is 166 MMT as the production required to meet utilization.

There are several problems in connection with the information on human consumption in Communist China: (1) How representative are official rations in relation to actual food grains made available to various groups of population? (2) The food surveys for certain geographical areas may be too limited in scope to represent the whole country. (3) The degree to which food grains were processed is not well defined.

In drawing conclusions one should not be unduly influenced by the apparent effort put into "The Great Leap." Such efforts, when applied in directions not suited to agricultural production, lead to a leap backward.

Thus, if the production in 1958 was in the vicinity of 174 MMT, it was greater than the average of 170 MMT for NARB Revised-M in 1931–37, but significantly less than the average of 182 MMT in 1929–33 for the *LU* Farm Survey-M.

## VIII. POPULATION

### *Population Estimates before 1949*

Estimates of the total population for mainland China before 1949 vary by as much as 100 million because of differing interpretations of incomplete census data.

In the early 1930's, 400 million was in common usage. The Food and Agriculture Organization of the United Nations (FAO), in computing a food balance sheet for 22 provinces of China for the period 1931–37, still used 400 million for 22 provinces (see Shen, *op. cit.*, pp. 378–89) and 36 million for Manchuria, 1935–38 (*ibid.*, pp. 382–83). As late as 1951, Dr. Shen assumed 450 million in computing nutritional requirements (*ibid.*, p. 172).

The Ministry of Interior of the Nationalist government reported a 463 million population in 1947. The Chinese Postal Administration's estimates by *hsien* in 1926 indicated a population of 485 million, a figure higher than any of the estimates from census data.

## Population Data from the LU Farm Survey

A possible check on these various estimates is the *LU* Farm Survey on density of population per square mile of crop area (cultivated area) for 100 farm households in each of 168 localities of 154 *hsien* (counties) in 22 provinces (see *LU-A*, p. 362, Table 2, col. 12,) and (*LU-B*, Table 3, col. 7, pp. 423–24).

The average of these densities is 1,485 per square mile. When weighted by crop area in each of the Eight Agricultural Areas of 22 provinces, a farm population of 489 million is obtained. Distribution of densities for each locality has been arranged by group intervals of 100, 500, and 1,000 persons to ascertain whether the mode or the median might be a better measure than the average to eliminate any possible undue influence on average density by a sizeable number of localities with high densities (Appendix, Table 8).

An inspection of these distributions indicates that *the modal group* of 1,000–1,999 persons, which contains 68 localities, might be the best representation of the data. However, the median of this group is 1,450 persons or only 35 persons fewer than the average of 1,485. A further inspection of this modal group by intervals of 100 persons reveals that 34 localities are within the interval of 1,000–1,299 persons, and another 34 localities in the interval of 1,300–1,999 persons. Hence, the density of the mid-number of localities in the modal group of 1,000–1,999 may be taken as 1,300 persons per square mile of crop area. This, multiplied by 339,644 square miles of cultivated land, gives a farm population of 441.5 million for the 22 provinces—the figure used in this monograph, rather than the average of 489 million to compute the total mainland population of 592 million, (Table 5).

TABLE 5. FARM, NONFARM AND TOTAL POPULATION FOR 22 PROVINCES AND MAINLAND CHINA, 1929–37

| Types of Population[1] | In Millions |
|---|---|
| I. Farm population | 473.6 |
| A. 22 provinces | 441.5 |
| B. Manchuria, Sikang and Sinkiang | 32.1 |
| II. Nonfarm population | 118.4 |
| A. 22 provinces | 110.4 |
| B. Manchuria, Sikang and Sinkiang | 8.0 |
| III. Total population | 592.0 |
| A. 22 provinces | 551.9 |
| B. Manchuria, Sikang and Sinkiang | 40.1 |

[1] The three types of population for the 22 provinces are computed from the *LU* Farm Survey of Farm population, 1929-33, Appendix Table 8, of 1,300 persons per square mile of cultivated land. Appendix Table 8, including note 1. The 1,300 multiplied by 339,644 square miles of cultivated land (Appendix Table 1, col. IV) equals 441.5 million (item I A). As described in the text, farm population is considered to be 80 per cent of total population, and the remaining 20 per cent as nonfarm population. The 441.5 million farm population divided by 80 per cent equals a total population of 551.9 million for the 22 provinces (item III A). The difference between 551.9 million and 441.5 million equals 110.4 million, the 20 per cent of total population as nonfarm population (item II A).

Official population for Manchuria (22) for 1931-37 and for Sikang and Sinkiang (21) for 1947 is 40.1 million. At 80 per cent of 40.1 million the farm population would be 32.1 million (item I B) and the nonfarm population at 20 per cent of total population would be 8 million (item II B).

The total population of 551.9 million for 22 provinces plus the 40.1 million for Manchuria, Sikang, and Sinkiang indicate a total population of 592 million for mainland China.

Although the Manchuria population is for 1931-37 and Sikang and Sinkiang population is for 1947, the total of 40.1 million may be an underestimate as was true of previous population estimates for all China. Therefore, one may consider the mainland China population in the order of 592 million as of 1929-33. For a further discussion of the use of 592 million in connection with NARB 1931-37 data, see "Comment" to Table 10.

The ratio of farm population to total population has commonly been considered 80 or 85 per cent. *LU* Farm Survey data for 63 *hsien* obtained from *hsien* records indicate 79.4 per cent in farm villages and hamlets, 10.7 in market towns, and 9.9 per cent in cities (see *LU-B,* p. 422, Table 2). Part of the market town population includes farmers, the exact proportion of which is not known. The Committee of Land Survey of the Kuomintang in cooperation with the Ministries of Finance and Interior carried out a survey by *hsien* under the chairmanship of Chen Li-fu during the years 1934-36. Data were obtained on cultivated area, population, number of persons per household, and production per unit of land. An abstract of 1,000 copies was published, for which the exact reference is not immediately available. The farm population was found to be 79.8 per cent of the total population, a percentage which includes farmers in market towns.

In the light of all available data, the figure 80 per cent to represent the proportion of farm to total population appears to be the most reasonable one and is used in this monograph. The Communist 1953 Census [15] gives a figure of 86 per cent for the rural population, but the distinction between rural and farm is not clear and, therefore, has doubtful validity as representing farm and nonfarm populations as used in this study.

The population estimate of 592 million for mainland China in 1929-33 (Table 5) is so much higher than previous estimates from incomplete censuses that many people, including some demographers, have found it difficult to accept. There are, nevertheless, three reasons why it should be given

[15] Leo A. Orleans, "The 1953 Chinese Census in Perspective," *Journal of Asia Studies,* Vol. XVI, No. 4 (Aug. 1957). This article contains tables of data by provinces for 20 different enumerations of China's population beginning with 1910-11 to 1953; and *Professional Manpower and Education in Communist China* (Washington, D. C.: Government Printing Office, 1960), chap. VIII. See also M. B. Ullman, *Cities of Mainland China: 1953 and 1958,* Bureau of Census, International Population Statistics Reports, Series p-95, No. 59 (Washington, D. C.: Government Printing Office Aug. 1961).

serious consideration. (1) It is based on a wide sample count
of farm persons on the land they farm. (2) The frequency
distribution indicates a skew curve which would be similar
to any other adequate sampling of density of population.
(3) The *LU*-Farm Survey data for production and consumption, obtained independently of each other and of population, cross-check closely, as will be observed in the discussion
of consumption.

## Communist China's Population

The Communist "end-of-the-year" population series for
1949–58, averaging 597 million, begins with 541.7 million in
1949, the source of which is not clear, and increases yearly
to 658 million in 1958. However arrived at, the 1949 figure
is an admission of a much higher one than any other estimate
from census data prior to 1949, but it is still below the
count of *LU* 592 million. The Communist 1953 census figure
of 582 million for midyear is undoubtedly more nearly correct than that of any previous census, and there is no reason
to suspect the 1953 Communist census figure as being too
high. The claimed rate of population increases after 1953
seems questionable in the light of factors possibly unfavorable to such natural increases. There may be a possibility
that part of the increases represent an upward adjustment of
an undercount in 1953. Since this is not the place to enter
into an extended discussion of population, the reader is
referred to separate studies by Orleans and Ullman [16] and
by Aird for an analysis of the 1953 census.

[16] *Ibid.*

## IX. FOOD GRAIN CONSUMPTION

*Comparative Amounts of All Food Grains Available per
Farm Capita Consumption for the 22 Provinces as Shown
in the LU and the NARB Food Surveys for the
Pre-Communist Period*

In studying this section, one should bear in mind that the
*LU* Farm Survey data on population, production, and farm
consumption were obtained from surveys that are independent of each other—that is, none have been computed
from the others.

Two sets of data on food consumption by the farm population permit us to check production against consumption.
The first is the *LU* Survey of farm food consumption for
1929–33 (Chapter 14 on "Nutrition" in *LU-A* and Chapter
3 on "Nutrition" in *LU-B*).

The second study is the NARB Food Survey of farm
families in 1937,[17] which also was obtained independently
of the NARB revised production data.

The absence of any comprehensive consumption studies
for cross-sections of the nonfarm population is the *LU* Survey's only missing link in a complete set of independent data
for cross-checking. Hence, the only check on population,
production, and farm consumption is the amount remaining
for the nonfarm population after deducting farm consumption from food available for the total population. The extent
to which the residual amount supplies the nonfarm population with reasonable amounts of food grains indicates the
degree to which data do cross-check.

The *LU* Survey of food consumption includes the average
annual amount of each food available for farm consumption
for 20 farm families in each of 136 localities, 131 *hsien,*

[17] National Agricultural Research Bureau, *op. cit.,* see note 5.

and 21 provinces, recorded in *LU-B,* Tables 17–1 to 17–136, pp. 86–121.

The *LU* enumerators who collected the data were instructed that the food schedules could be completed for families other than those surveyed for farm data in order to avoid too many questions for the same family. No record, however, is available of the proportion of families included in the food study that were the same as those from which farm data were obtained, although the families were in the same type of farming area.

The amounts of each food grain have been compiled for this monograph by each of the Eight Agricultural Areas and weighted by the farm population of each Area to obtain the average amount of 270 kilograms per farm capita per year (Appendix Table 9, col. III).

The NARB data on farm family consumption in *A Study of the Consumption of Staple Food Products in Rural China* are based on 3,278 reports representing 1,042 *hsien* from 22 provinces.[18] The report states that the data were obtained in the summer of 1937, "for the usual consumption, not consumption for any particular year"; and that "old and young" were included in the survey. Both of these approaches are logical, because farmers do have sayings about the quantities of food consumed by a family of a certain size or per person, young and old.[19]

The NARB annual amount of food grains available for consumption per farm capita is reported as 296.4 kilograms (Appendix Table 9, col. IV). The note to Table 1 in the NARB report states: "These figures are first averaged by *hsien,* next by provinces, and then for China as a whole." [20] A check has been made for this monograph on the method of obtaining the average for China. The average for each

[18] *Ibid.*

[19] John Lossing Buck, *Chinese Farm Economy* (Chicago: University of Chicago Press, 1930), p. 355.

[20] National Agricultural Research Bureau, *op. cit.,* see note 5.

food grain for each province, multiplied by the number of *hsien* studied in each province, when totaled and divided by the total number of *hsien,* give the average amount of each individual food grain for the 22 provinces. All these totals for each food grain add up to the 296.4 kilograms referred to above. On the other hand, the sum of the averages of each food grain for each province divided by the 22 provinces indicates an average of 287 kilograms (Appendix Table 9, col. V), and different averages for each group of food grains than those listed of that table in col. IV. A better type of average would be one obtained by weighted consumption per farm capita by farm population in areas of similar consumption, as was done for *LU* Food Survey data by the *LU* Eight Agricultural Areas. Since the NARB data are presented only by provinces and because parts of a number of provinces are located in at least two different areas, weighting by provincial total population would still fall short of a correct average (Table 9, note [f]). As explained, however, in this note, an apparently acceptable average for NARB reports of consumption has been obtained in col. VI of Appendix Table 9.

The method described gives an average of 286 kilograms of all food grains per farm capita. The weighted averages for rice, wheat, and potatoes are similar to those for *LU* column III in Appendix Table 9 but are significantly different for miscellaneous grains, because of the NARB Food study's higher reported amount of 123 kilograms as the average consumption by localities (Appendix Table 9, col. IV) as compared with the *LU* Food Survey's average of 92 kilograms for localities (Appendix Table 9, col. II). By the above mentioned method of weighting, the difference for miscellaneous grains is narrowed to 81 kilograms for NARB compared with the 93 kilograms for *LU*. This is a difference of 16 kilograms per farm capita, which is the same as that between the average of 286 kilograms and the *LU* weighted

average of 270 kilograms. This difference implies too high
a reporting of consumption of miscellaneous grains or too
low a production of miscellaneous grains. The subsequent
discussion may clarify this point.

### Comparative Amounts of Food Grains Available for Consumption by the Farm, Nonfarm, and Total Populations (Table 1 and Appendix Table 10)

As previously mentioned, the test of data on production,
population, and consumption is the degree to which they
cross-check, providing the relationship is not a spurious one,
as in the case of the FAO food balance sheet quoted by Shen
*(op. cit.)*, in which quantities for both production and population were too low. The amount of food grains available for
human consumption, minus the amount reported for farm
family consumption, is the only apparently reliable text in
the absence of comprehensive food surveys for the nonfarm
population.

As for the pre-Communist sources of data for mainland
China, only two leave enough food grains for the nonfarm
population after deducting grains for farm consumption, i.e.,
the *LU* Farm Survey with 27 million metric tons and the
Combined Estimates with 32 million metric tons, the latter
amount being too large on the basis of a total population of
592 million (Table 1).

The Communist amounts for farm, nonfarm, and total
population are all less than those in the *LU* Farm Survey
and Combined Estimates, but the proportion between the
farm and nonfarm population is similar to the *LU* Farm
Survey figures. The reason for this is that in the absence of
sufficient data on farm food consumption for the Communist
period, the same percentage of food available for farm consumption is used as that given in *LU* Survey-M, col. V in
Appendix Table 11, although it may be different (see Table

1). Another assumption is that the proportion of 80 per cent of farm population to the total population is also the same as for the *LU* Farm Survey (Table 5), even though the Communists claim 86 per cent as "rural," which is an indefinite term.

*Comparative Quantities for Each of the Four Groups of Food Grains Available for Food for the Farm, Nonfarm, and Total Populations for 22 Provinces, China (Appendix Table 10)*

Appendix Table 10 provides a detailed analysis of food grains remaining for the nonfarm population for each of the four groups of food grains for the 22 provinces dealt with by the two separate studies of farm family consumption. Appendix Table 10 also depicts the relationship between production and consumption for five different combinations of sources for production and for farm food consumption.

For a discussion of the use of the NARB Revised production for 1931–37 and comparison of these figures with the NARB Food Survey data collected in 1937 for the most usual consumption, see "Comment" to Appendix Table 10.

Among all these combinations, the *LU* Farm Survey and the *LU* Food Survey are the only sources indicating that enough rice was produced for the nonfarm population. The other combinations show a great insufficiency of rice for the nonfarm population from minus 4.1 million metric tons for NARB data to plus 3 million metric tons. Since rice consumption is similar for both the *LU* and the NARB Food Surveys, the insufficiency of rice for the nonfarm population apparently is due to a low production figure for rice.

The NARB data for miscellaneous grains indicate a minus 1.1 million metric tons for the nonfarm population caused chiefly by a very high consumption figure for the farm population. But the computation of the Combined Estimates with the NARB Food Survey indicates 15.3 million metric tons of miscellaneous grains for the nonfarm population, due to a very high production figure for miscellaneous grains in the Combined Estimates. It appears doubtful, however, that as large a proportion of 15.3 million metric tons is consumed by the nonfarm population.

A potato consumption of 4.6 million metric tons and 4.4 million metric tons by the nonfarm population for two of the combinations also appears unrealistic in light of reports of either too high production or too low farm consumption, or omission of some other uses of potatoes.

This cross-checking of data by production, farm consumption, and population leads to the following conclusions: (1) rice production is too low for the NARB Revised and the Combined Estimates; (2) the NARB Food Survey on consumption of miscellaneous grains is too high in relation to the NARB Revised production and the *LU* Farm Survey of production; (3) production of miscellaneous grains is too high for crop estimates.

It now appears that the *LU* Survey-M data are the most appropriate for computing available calories for comparison with calories available according to the Communist 1949–58 production figures.

*Comparative Amounts of Processed Food Grains and Calories Available for Consumption from the LU Farm Survey-M, 1929–33, and the Communist Data, 1949–58, Mainland China* (Table 1, Part II, and Appendix Tables 11 and 12)

Because the *LU* Farm and Food Surveys are the only pre-Communist sources of data indicating a reasonable amount of food grains for the nonfarm population, they are used for comparing quantities of production data. The computations from production to obtain processed amounts and calories available per capita per day for farm, nonfarm, and total population appear in Appendix Tables 11 and 13 with notes on the methods used in the calculations.

The quantities of unprocessed food grains available for consumption annually per capita for the total population are 262 kilograms for the *LU* Farm Survey-M and 231 kilograms for the Communist data.

The amount of 231 kilograms of unprocessed food grains per capita computed from the Communist production data are nearly the same as the 228 kilograms of unprocessed food grains per capita computed from Dr. Wu's data (see note on col. 9 to Table 1 on Communist food rations in his accompanying essay, "The Economics of Mainland China's Agriculture").

The quantities of processed grains available annually for the total population are 210 kilograms for the *LU* Farm Survey-M and 186 kilograms for the Communist 1949–58 period; on a per capita per diem basis, the corresponding figures are 575 and 509 grams.

The number of calories available from the total production of food grains reported by the *LU* Farm Survey-M and in the Communist statistics after deducting uses other than for food are, respectively, 2,023 and 1,776 per capita per day.

If net imports for the *LU* Farm Survey period and net exports for the Communist period are included in the computations, the per capita calories from food grains for the former would be 2,046, and for the latter 1,715 (Appendix Table 11, note 10 and Appendix Table 12, note 10).

The calories available per capita for total population from all food may be computed as explained in note 10 to Appendix Table 11. They amount to 2,410 calories for the *LU* Farm Survey-M after including net imports, and 2,017 calories per capita for the Communist period after subtracting net exports, or 83.7 per cent of the *LU* Farm Survey-M calories (Table 1, part II, and Appendix Tables 11 and 12, parts II, Sections C).

Because the same factors are used for computing food grains available and for processing in both sets of data, any other factors for both sets of data, any other factors for both sets of data would not change this percentage relationship. As explained in notes to Appendix Table 11, these amounts of calories do not indicate the actual intake of calories. They are the caloric values of the food grains available for consumption. These are, of course, losses before actual consumption, and there may be a difference in metabolism for so large a vegetarian diet and, particularly so, for coarse grains consumed by farmers. Hence, these amounts of calories may be considered to be higher than the actual intake of calories.

## X. SUMMARY

The public has been misled by the boasts of the Chinese Communists and by their food grain production statistics for 1949–58 which began with too low a figure in 1949 and then increased every year until they reported the greatly exaggerated amount in 1958.

The 1949 amount was apparently based on the National Agricultural Research Bureau's estimates of production which were too low because the official land statistics of cultivated land recorded only three-fourths of all cultivated land. This omission of unregistered land was discovered in the study, *Land Utilization in China*. The Communists used a corrected figure for cultivated land for 1949, but somehow failed to make a corresponding correction in the amount of production. Hence, their series of production data record increases that are primarily statistical.

Moreover, the Communist 1949–58 figure for food grain production is only 163 million metric tons which may be compared with two pre-Communist sources of data. One is the 182 million metric tons computed from the *Land Utiliza-*

*tion in China* study for 22 provinces in 1929–33 and from official production figures for Manchuria, Sikang, and Sinkiang. The other is the 170 million metric tons obtained from the National Agricultural Research Bureau Estimates for 1931–37 for 22 provinces—but corrected in this monograph for omission of land—and from official data for Manchuria, Sikang, and Sinkiang.

The Chinese Communists, in their statistical effort to make production agree with their ideology, have claimed a significantly smaller average production for 1949–58 than for the pre-Communist periods of 1929–33 and 1931–37.

The total population estimate for 1929–33 based on the *Land Utilization in China* farm survey of farm population density per square mile of cultivated land is 592 million which includes the population of Manchuria, Sikang, and Sinkiang, compared with the Communist claim of a 597 million year-end population for 1949–58. The commonly accepted population figure in the early 1930's was 400 to 450 million.

A cross-check of production and farm consumption totals for each of the four groups of food grains—rice, wheat, miscellaneous grains, and potatoes—given by pre-Communist sources indicates that the *LU* Farm Survey-M data show the most realistic amounts remaining for the nonfarm population. The estimates of the National Agricultural Research Bureau for 1931–37 suggest too small a rice production compared with rice consumption, and possibly too high a farm consumption of miscellaneous grains. Therefore, the data from the *Land Utilization in China* study, plus data for Manchuria, Sikang, and Sinkiang are used for comparison with Communist production, consumption, and population figures for mainland China.

The *Land Utilization in China* data on per capita consumption of food grains for a total population of 592 million in 1929–33 indicate that 262 kilograms of unprocessed grain per capita were available annually, and that for the Communist period of 1949–58 for a year-end population of 597 million, 231 kilograms were available. In terms of calories per capita from all foods for the entire population, *LU* data indicate that 2,410 calories were available, including net imports; the Communist data indicate that 2,017 cal. per capita were available, excluding net exports, or 83.7 per cent of 2,410 cal. These calories represent availability, not actual intake, which would be less because of losses and possibly a less efficient metabolism for such a highly vegetarian diet.

If the actual 1949–58 production was greater than 163 million metric tons, the above difference would be smaller, providing the excess did not disappear into hoarded stocks. The meager information on Communist rations implies that the calories available to the population may have been about the same as computed above.

The degree of accuracy of the findings in this study depends on the reliability of the source data and on the accuracy of the factors for other than food uses such as those for processing food grains; for the proportion of farm population to total population; and for the correction factor for the National Agricultural Research Bureau figure of cultivated land.

As a by-product, the findings in this paper indicate the value of the *Land Utilization in China* field sample surveys independent of official data, and especially so since the cultivated land, population, production, and consumption data obtained in these surveys cross-check so closely. They also reveal the value of the National Agricultural Research Bureau reports on farm food consumption as a check on its production data and for comparison with the *Land Utilization in China* food studies.

The apparent severe downward trend in Communist production that began in 1958 has led to extreme hunger and malnutrition, and possibly some starvation. This collapse in Communist food production may be ascribed to the following: the reorganization of the farm production unit into large Agricultural Producers' Cooperatives and later into large Communes; to the absence of sufficient incentives; to wrong directives from Peking on what and how to plant; and in 1960–61, partly to natural calamities.

Reported improvement in production in 1962 and 1963 is undoubtedly due to abandonment of the large Communes and the allocation of small plots of land to farmers with freedom to sell the produce thereof in the open market, and, possibly, to favorable weather. This apparent partial recovery is still below the *LU* Farm Survey production figure of 181.9 million metric tons for 1929–33.

If the Communists had left farming to the farmers and had concentrated on providing them with the necessary production supplies; adequate credit, including land credit; extension education in tested and improved agricultural techniques; and had allowed them control of their own organizations, agricultural progress could have been great. The Chinese in Taiwan and the Japanese in their homeland have provided examples of effective land reforms with a constant increase in food production, leaving the management of agriculture to those who best know the art of farming—the farmers themselves.

APPENDIX TABLE 1. CULTIVATED AREA, INDEX OF MULTIPLE CROPPING AND CROP HECTARES GROUPED BY LU EIGHT AGRICULTURAL AREAS (22 PROVINCES), CHINA

| Regions and Areas | NARB square miles[1] | LU Correction factors[2] | Cultivated Land | | | LU Farm Survey Index of Multiple cropping[5] | LU Farm Survey crop hectare area | |
|---|---|---|---|---|---|---|---|---|
| | | | Square miles[3] | Revised[4] Hectares (m) | Per Cent | | Hectare (m) | Per cent |
| I | II | III | IV | V | VI | VII | VIII | IX |
| Eight Agricultural Areas (22 provinces) | 254,018 | 1.337 | 339,644 | 88.0 | 100.0 | 146.8 | 129.2 | 100.0 |
| Wheat Region | 124,335 | 1.390 | 172,910 | 44.8 | 50.9 | 131.0 | 58.7 | 45.0 |
| Rice Region | 129,683 | 1.286 | 166,728 | 43.2 | 49.1 | 163.2 | 70.5 | 55.0 |
| Wheat Region Areas: | | | | | | | | |
| Spring Wheat | 16,336 | 1.35 | 22,054 | 5.7 | 6.5 | 107.0 | 6.1 | 4.7 |
| Winter Wheat-millet | 23,607 | 1.35 | 31,869 | 8.3 | 9.4 | 118.0 | 9.8 | 7.5 |
| Winter Wheat-kaoliang | 84,392 | 1.41 | 118,993 | 30.8 | 35.0 | 139.0 | 42.8 | 32.8 |
| Rice Region Areas: | | | | | | | | |
| Yangtze Rice-wheat | 35,068 | 1.15 | 40,328 | 10.5 | 11.9 | 163.1 | 17.1 | 13.3 |
| Rice-tea | 36,122 | 1.18 | 42,624 | 11.0 | 12.6 | 163.3 | 18.0 | 14.2 |
| Szechwan Rice | 27,188 | 1.75 | 47,579 | 12.3 | 14.0 | 167.0 | 20.5 | 15.7 |
| Double Cropping Rice | 17,103 | 1.12 | 19,155 | 5.0 | 5.6 | 164.3 | 8.2 | 6.7 |
| Southwestern Rice | 14,202 | 1.20 | 17,042 | 4.4 | 5.0 | 152.0 | 6.7 | 5.1 |

[1] Computed for the LU Eight Agricultural Areas from the Statistical Monthly data by hsien. The total square miles of 254, 018 is 65.8 million hectares the number used by NARB to compute production, p. 30, Table 2, Col. III (see note 2B).

[2] See the text topic "cultivated land" for explanation of the LU correction factor, p. 30, Table 2, Col. III (see note 2A), or p. 164, Table 2, Col. III, the reciprocal of which gives the correction factor.

[3] From p. 167, Table 5, Col. III (see note 2A).

[4] Corrected square miles, Col. IV, converted to hectares at 259 hectares per square mile.

[5] From Table 5, p. 216 (see note 2A) except for downward adjustments in crop hectares for interplanted rice which in this table is considered as one crop hectare rather than two, because the early and late crops share the one hectare, half and half. The reductions made in Col. 7 from Table 5, p. 216 (see note 2A) are 0.2 million hectares for Yangtze Rice-wheat area, 0.6 million hectares for the Rice-tea area and 0.6 million hectares for the Double Cropping Rice area.

[6] For each area, Col. V, multiplied by Col. VII. The term "crop hectares" represents the number of hectares in one, two, or more crops each year.

Comment: There is great variation in the correction factors between Areas. The data are from 148 hsien and it is possible that a larger sample would indicate different factors, although the average of 133.7 may be too low rather than too high as discussed in the section on which the amount of cultivated land at any particular time. Comparatively small

APPENDIX TABLE 2. COMPARISON OF CULTIVATED LAND AREA BY SOURCES OF DATA, MAINLAND CHINA
(FOR THE PRE-COMMUNIST PERIOD OF 1929–37 AND THE COMMUNIST PERIOD OF 1949–58)

| Sources of data[1] | Hectares of cultivated land (m) II | Sources of data (cont'd) | Hectares of cultivated land (cont'd) (m) II |
|---|---|---|---|
| **I** | | **I** | **II** |
| Pre-Communist period | | Communist period | |
| | | *The Great Ten Years* | |
| *Statistical Monthly*, 1929-32[2] | 76.7 | 1949-58 | 107.0 |
| NARB Estimates-M, 1931-37[3] | 80.2 | 1949 | 97.9 |
| NARB Revised-M, 1931-37[4] | 102.4 | 1950 | 100.4 |
| Combined Estimates-M, 1929-33[5] | 102.4 | 1951 | 103.7 |
| LU Farm Survey-M 1929-33[6] | 102.4 | 1952 | 107.9 |
| | | 1953 | 108.5 |
| | | 1954 | 109.4 |
| | | 1955 | 110.2 |
| | | 1956 | 112.0 |
| | | 1957 | 111.8 |
| | | 1958 | 107.8 |

[1] Pre-Communist period data for each of lines 2-5 are for two areas, one for the 22 provinces (designated by sources as NARB Estimates, NARB Revised, Combined Estimates, and LU Farm Survey), and the other, for official data for Manchuria, Sikang, and Sinkiang (denoted by the letter "M" placed after each of these sources) to represent cultivated land for mainland China. This nomenclature for sources of data is maintained in all tables for mainland China. The amounts of cultivated land for the 22 provinces may be computed by subtracting the amounts for Manchuria, Sikang and Sinkiang in Appendix Table 3.

[2] *The Statistical Monthly* data (see note 3) on cultivated land, crop hectares and production of each crop, are estimates according to the introduction, by *hsien*, based largely on accumulated reports of *hsien* governments, postmasters and farmers, collected by the Bureau of Statistics, National Government of China (1931-32) for mainland China. Some of the figures are a revision of data published under the title "An Estimate of China's Farm and Crops" (see note 4) and, also, once published in the *Statistical Monthly* of the Legislative Yuan. The following statement in the introduction applies, in general, also to the *Statistical Monthly Data*.

"Since the work lasted for three years, no estimates refer to any specific year. For some *hsiens*, estimates on farm households and cultivated land were based on data referring to as far back as 1912.

**Notes Continued on Following Page**

## NOTES TO APPENDIX TABLE 2 CONT'D.

"The acreage and production of crops refer to the average years, the most prevalent years in the last decade."

Because of lack of complete data, the three provinces of Kwangsi, Sikang, and Tsinghai were omitted. Also the number of *hsien* omitted in other provinces were ten for Sinkiang, four in Yunnan and one each in Heilungkiang and Kweichow. The 76.7 million hectares are underestimates of cultivated land for mainland China for the period 1929-31 for reasons of territory not included and because of unregistered land not included. However, the amount of territory entirely omitted is not as great as it appears, because of pastoral use of land in several of these areas.

[3] The 80.2 million hectares consists of 65.8 million hectares for NARB Estimates for 22 provinces and 14.4 million hectares for Manchuria, Sikang and Sinkiang (Appendix Table 3). The 65.8 million hectares for 22 provinces represents an increase for some cultivated land omitted in the *Statistical Monthly* for these same provinces.

[4] The 65.8 million hectares for NARB Estimates has been revised in this study under the caption "NARB Revised" by including unregistered cultivated land estimated by the *LU* investigators to be at least one-fourth of all cultivated area. The correction factor is 1.337 making a total of 88 million hectares. The addition of 14.4 million hectares for Manchuria, Sikang, and Sinkiang (Appendix Table 3) indicates a NARB Revised-M cultivated land area of 102.4 million hectares for mainland China. No corrections have been made to the 14.4 million hectares for any unregistered land that may have existed in these three areas.

[5] The same amount of cultivated land as for the *LU* Farm Survey-M.

[6] The cultivated land area for the *LU* Farm Survey-M is the same as for NARB Revised-M since the latter is based on the *LU* correction factor of 133.7 per cent. Thus, 88 million hectares for the Eight Agricultural Areas (22 provinces) plus 14.4 million hectares (Appendix Table 3) equals 102.4 million hectares for mainland China.

[7] *The Great Ten Years*, p. 113. The average is computed for this study from the annual data.

APPENDIX TABLE 3. CULTIVATED LAND, CROP HECTARES AND PRODUCTION OF FOOD GRAINS FOR MANCHURIA, SIKANG AND SINKIANG, 1931–37

| Areas | Cultivated land in hectares (m) | Crop hectares (m) | | | | |
|---|---|---|---|---|---|---|
| | | Rice | Wheat | Miscellaneous | Potatoes | Total |
| I | II | III | IV | V | VI | VII |
| Manchuria[1] | 13.1 | 0.2 | 1.4 | 7.7 | 1.0 | 10.3 |
| Sikang[2] | 0.3 | * | * | 0.2 | * | 0.2 |
| Sinkiang[2] | 1.0 | 0.1 | 0.3 | 0.3 | 0.1 | 0.8 |
| Total | 14.4 | 0.3 | 1.7 | 8.2 | 1.1 | 11.3 |
| | | Production (*MMT*) | | | | |
| Manchuria[3] | | 0.4 | 1.0 | 10.3 | 1.9 | 13.6 |
| Sikang[4] | | * | * | 0.3 | * | 0.3 |
| Sinkiang[4] | | 0.2 | 0.5 | 0.3 | * | 1.0 |
| Total | | 0.6 | 1.5 | 10.9 | 1.9 | 14.9 |

* Probably less than 0.1 million hectares or 0.1 million metric tons.
[1] *The Manchukuo year-book* for 1942.
[2] Reference p. 142 for 1947 (1). Crop hectares are computed at 80 per cent of the cultivated land, the same proportion as *LU* data for Kansu Province.
[3] *The Manchukukuo year-book* for 1942. Potatoes are computed with assumed yield of 1,712 kg grain-equivalent per crop hectare, similar to the Spring Wheat Area, p. 223, Table 9 (See Note 2B).
[4] Production is estimated on basis of Manchuria yields per hectare, except potatoes which are estimated as the same average for the Spring Wheat Area for irrigated and non-irrigated potatoes, pp. 223-226, Table 14.
The data for Sikang and Sinkiang are questionable but these dates or any other reasonably accurate data, would have little influence on the total food grains for mainland China.

APPENDIX TABLE 4. COMPARISON OF CROP HECTARES IN FOOD GRAINS BY SOURCES OF DATA, MAINLAND CHINA[1] (FOR THE PRE-COMMUNIST PERIOD OF 1929–37 AND THE COMMUNIST PERIOD OF 1949–58)

| Sources of Data | Crop hectares in food grains (millions) | | | | | Index or multiple cropping[8] |
|---|---|---|---|---|---|---|
| I | Rice | Wheat | Miscellaneous | Potatoes | Total | |
| | II | III | IV | V | VI | VII |
| **Pre-Communist period** | | | | | | |
| Statistical Monthly, 1929–32[2] | 19.8 | 21.0 | 37.1 | 2.0 | 79.9 | 104 |
| NARB Estimates-M, 1931–37[3] | 20.1 | 21.9 | 42.7 | 3.7 | 88.4 | 110 |
| NARB Revised-M, 1931–37[4] | 26.8 | 28.7 | 54.3 | 4.6 | 114.4 | 112 |
| Combined Estimates-M, 1929–33[5] | 27.0 | 28.2 | 62.9 | 6.2 | 124.3 | 121 |
| LU Survey-M, 1929–33[6] | 31.9 | 23.0 | 50.1 | 5.8 | 110.8 | 108 |
| **Communist period[7]** | | | | | | |
| The Great Ten Years, 1949–58 | 29.2 | 25.3 | 49.8 | 9.8 | 114.1 | 106 |
| 1949 | 25.7 | 21.5 | 47.4 | 7.0 | 101.6 | 104 |
| 1950 | 26.1 | 22.8 | 48.2 | 7.7 | 104.8 | 104 |
| 1951 | 26.9 | 23.1 | 48.7 | 8.3 | 107.0 | 103 |
| 1952 | 28.4 | 24.8 | 50.4 | 8.7 | 112.3 | 104 |
| 1953 | 28.3 | 25.6 | 51.3 | 9.0 | 114.3 | 105 |
| 1954 | 28.7 | 26.9 | 50.9 | 9.8 | 116.3 | 106 |
| 1955 | 29.2 | 26.7 | 52.5 | 10.0 | 118.4 | 106 |
| 1956 | 33.3 | 27.3 | 52.7 | 11.0 | 124.3 | 111 |
| 1957 | 32.3 | 27.5 | 50.6 | 10.5 | 120.9 | 108 |
| 1958 | 32.7 | 26.6 | 45.7 | 16.3 | 121.3 | 112 |

[1] The data for lines 2–5 are for 22 provinces of China to which has been added data for Manchuria, Sikang, and Sinkiang from Appendix Table 3.

The food grain crops are classified as rice, wheat, miscellaneous, and potatoes for comparison with Communist statistics. Production of potatoes reduced by one-fourth, is considered as grain-equivalent. The miscellaneous crops include barley, green beans (mung), broad beans, buckwheat, corn, kaoliang, millet, broomcorn millet, non-glutinous proso millet, proso millet, oats, and field peas. Broomcorn and non-glutinous proso millet were not listed in the Statistical Monthly, or in NARB Estimates and proso millet was not listed in the Statistical Monthly. Potatoes include sweet and white (or Irish) potatoes. The term "food grains" does not include a number of other minor crops, the seeds of which are used for food, entirely, or partially, such as soybeans, sesame, rapeseed, and lentils or squash and taroes.

According to the *LU* Farm Survey, available calories from the "food grains" constitute 87.8 per cent of total food energy, whereas 97.7 per cent of all food energy for the farm population is from the vegetable kingdom, Table 6, p. 413 (See Note 2A).

2 *The Statistical Monthly*, pp. 2-3 (See Note 3), contains data by provinces on acreage and production of the important crops, but Kwangsi and Tsinghai Provinces and some 16 *hsien* chiefly in border provinces are not included because of incomplete data.

3 The NARB Estimates for crop hectares in the 22 provinces are from two sources both of which are from NARB original data. The main source is the crop hectares for each principal crop recorded in Appendix Table 3 (See Note 1).

The second source is for the minor crops of green beans (mung), buckwheat, and white potatoes, production of which is given in the FAO food balance sheet for China, Appendix Table 4 (See Note 1). Crop hectares for these three crops are computed from production on basis of *LU* yields. Total NARB Estimates-M crop hectares for the mainland crop hectares are obtained by adding crop hectares for Manchuria, Sikang, and Sinkiang (Appendix Table 3). Some minor food grain crops are not included in NARB Estimates.

NARB determined crop hectares for each crop from estimated percentages of crop area (cultivated land) in each crop obtained from a special survey by NARB reporters, but these estimates were never published. These percentages were multiplied by 65.8 million hectares of cultivated land to obtain crop hectares in each crop. They can be determined by dividing hectares in each crop by 65.8 million hectares.

4 The NARB Revised crop hectares are obtained by multiplying NARB Estimates of crop hectares for 22 provinces by the *LU* correction factor of 1.337 and adding the crop hectares in Appendix Table 3 for Manchuria, Sikang, and Sinkiang. They may also be obtained by multiplying the percentages of crop area in each crop for the 22 provinces by the revised cultivated area of 88 million hectares for the 22 provinces.

5 These data are from Combined Estimates of per cent of crop area in each crop from NARB unpublished Crop Report Data and unpublished *LU* Agricultural Survey Data. Both sets of data are from estimates by local people acquainted with farming in a total of 830 localities, 737 *hsien*, 22 provinces, Table 3, pp. 211-12 (SSe Note 2A). A similar table, which gives the number of localities from which estimates were obtained, by Agricultural Areas, is Table 4, p. 183 (See Note 2B). These percentages when multiplied by *LU* 88 million hectares cultivated land indicate the crop hectares for each crop in the 22 provinces to which are added crop hectares for Manchuria, Sikang, and Sinkiang (Appendix Table 1) to obtain crop hectares for mainland China.

6 *LU* Farm Survey crop hectares are computed from the average percentages of crop hectares in each crop on 16,456 farms in 164 localities, 151 *hsien*, 22 provinces, China, Table 2, p. 174 (see Note 2B). These average percentages for each Agricultural Area have been weighted by the total crop hectares in each Agricultural Area (Appendix Table 1) to obtain the total crop hectares for each crop. This method of weighting in place by number of localities studied in each Area is considered to be more representative for individual crops because the number of localities studied are not entirely proportional to the crop hectares in each area. However, the total crop hectares by each method is almost identical. The original information is from farmers for crops on the land they farmed. Questions asked farmers were cross-checked, such as, area in each crop and total area; total production of each crop and yield per unit of land. The percentages of crop hectares, in Table 3, p. 174 (See Note 2B) were computed from the total number of crop hectares reported by farmers in each locality.

The area in interplanted rice which consists of an early planting in widely spaced rows and a later planting between these rows with harvesting of each at different times, is considered as one crop hectare. Localities with interplanting of rice are indicated by footnotes to Table 6, pp. 192-206 (See Note 2B). Double cropping of rice, where a late crop follows after the harvest of an early crop, is considered as two crop hectares.

7 From p. 114, *The Great Ten Years* (See Note 9). The averages are computed for this study from the annual data.

8 This index is for food grains only and should not be confused with the index of multiple cropping for all crops. It is obtained by dividing col. VI in this table by col. II, Appendix Table 2.

APPENDIX TABLE 5. COMPARISON OF PRODUCTION OF FOOD GRAINS BY SOURCES OF DATA, MAINLAND CHINA
(FOR THE PRE-COMMUNIST PERIOD OF 1929-37 AND THE COMMUNIST PERIOD OF 1949-58)

| Sources of data[1] | Food grains (in millions metric tons) | | | | |
| | Rice (unhulled) | Wheat | Miscellaneous | Potatoes | Total |
| I | II | III | IV | V | VI |
| **Pre-Communist period** | | | | | |
| *Statistical Monthly*, 1929-32[2] | 58.3 | 25.3 | 50.2 | 3.1 | 136.9 |
| NARB Estimates-M, 1931-37[3] | 50.7 | 23.2 | 50.1 | 7.0 | 131.0 |
| NARB Revised-M, 1931-37[4] | 67.8 | 30.6 | 63.2 | 8.7 | 170.3 |
| Combined Estimates-M, 1929-33[6] | 74.7 | 29.8 | 72.9 | 11.8 | 189.2 |
| LU Farm Survey-M, 1929-33[5] | 88.3 | 24.2 | 58.4 | 11.0 | 181.9 |
| **Communist period[7]** | | | | | |
| *The Great Ten Years* 1949-58 | | | | | |
| 1949 | 73.6 | 20.6 | 49.6 | 19.4 | 163.2 |
| 1950 | 48.7 | 13.8 | 35.8 | 9.9 | 108.2 |
| 1951 | 55.1 | 14.5 | 42.7 | 12.4 | 124.7 |
| 1952 | 60.6 | 17.3 | 43.2 | 14.0 | 135.1 |
| 1953 | 68.4 | 18.1 | 51.5 | 16.4 | 154.4 |
| 1954 | 71.2 | 18.3 | 50.7 | 16.7 | 156.9 |
| 1955 | 70.9 | 23.5 | 49.2 | 17.0 | 160.5 |
| 1956 | 78.0 | 23.0 | 55.0 | 18.9 | 174.9 |
| 1957 | 82.5 | 24.8 | 53.4 | 21.9 | 182.6 |
| 1958 | 86.8 | 23.7 | 52.6 | 21.9 | 185.0 |
| | 113.7 | 29.0 | 62.0 | 45.4 | 250.0 |

Notes to Appendix Table 5

[1] The data for lines 2-5 are for 22 provinces of China to which has been added data for Manchuria, Sikang, and Sinkiang from Appendix Table 3.

[2] From production data for each crop, pp. 2-3 (see note 3).

[3] The NARB Estimates-M include production of principal crops quoted by Shen, pp. 374-75. Appendix Table 2 (see note 1) and for NARB minor crops of buckwheat, green beans (mung), and white potatoes pp. 378-79, Appendix Table 4 (see note 1) for 22 provinces, plus production for Manchuria, Sikang, and Sinkiang in Appendix Table 3.

[4] NARB Revised crop hectares for 22 provinces multiplied by NARB Estimates of yields per crop hectare of 2,534 kg for rice, 1,097 kg for wheat, 1,135 kg for miscellaneous, and 1,975 kg for potatoes indicates NARB Revised production for 22 provinces. These yields are obtained by dividing NARB Estimates of production by NARB Estimates of crop hectares (using all digits) Appendix Tables 3 and 4 (see note 1). Production for Manchuria, Sikang, and Sinkiang in Appendix Table 3 added to the production for 22 provinces gives the production for mainland China.

[5] To obtain production, crop hectares for *LU* Farm Survey for 22 provinces are multiplied by *LU* Farm Survey "most frequent yields" of 2,775 kg (median) for rice, 1,067 kg for wheat, 1,134 kg for miscellaneous, and 1,936 kg for potatoes, pp. 209-10, Table 9 (see note 2B). This production plus production for Manchuria, Sikang, and Sinkiang (Appendix Table 3) indicates total production for mainland China. The *LU* Farm Survey yields are the "most frequent yields" occurring on the farmers' land during the previous ten year period, Appendix 209-10, Table 9 (see note 2B).

[6] The crop hectares for Combined Estimates, pp. 211-12, Table 3, are multiplied by the *LU* Farm Survey yields, as in note 5 above. Production for Manchuria, Sikang, and Sinkiang is added to obtain mainland production.

[7] Production reported, p. 105 of *The Great Ten Years* (see note 9).

APPENDIX TABLE 6. COMPARISON OF YIELDS OF FOOD GRAIN CROPS BY SOURCES OF DATA, MAINLAND CHINA (FOR THE PRE-COMMUNIST PERIOD OF 1929-37 AND THE COMMUNIST PERIOD OF 1949-58)

| Sources of data | Yields of food grains per crop hectare (in kilograms)[1] | | | | |
|---|---|---|---|---|---|
| | Rice (unhulled) | Wheat | Miscellaneous | Potatoes | All food grains |
| I | II | III | IV | V | VI |
| **Pre-Communist period** | | | | | |
| Statistical Monthly, 1929-32 | 2,936 | 1,205 | 1,353 | 1,550 | 1,713 |
| NARB Estimates-M, 1931-37 | 2,493 | 1,059 | 1,173 | 1,892 | 1,482 |
| NARB Revised-M, 1931-37 | 2,530 | 1,066 | 1,164 | 1,977 | 1,489 |
| Combined Estimates-M, 1929-33 | 2,767 | 1,057 | 1,159 | 1,903 | 1,522 |
| LU Farm Survey-M, 1929-33 | 2,768 | 1,052 | 1,166 | 1,896 | 1,642 |
| **Communist period** | | | | | |
| The Great Ten Years, 1949-58 | 2,520 | 814 | 996 | 1,980 | 1,430 |
| 1949 | 1,894 | 642 | 755 | 1,414 | 1,065 |
| 1950 | 2,111 | 637 | 886 | 1,610 | 1,191 |
| 1951 | 2,021 | 749 | 887 | 1,687 | 1,263 |
| 1952 | 2,408 | 730 | 1,022 | 1,885 | 1,377 |
| 1953 | 2,517 | 715 | 978 | 1,856 | 1,373 |
| 1954 | 2,470 | 874 | 965 | 1,735 | 1,380 |
| 1955 | 2,670 | 861 | 1,048 | 1,890 | 1,494 |
| 1956 | 2,477 | 908 | 1,013 | 1,991 | 1,471 |
| 1957 | 2,687 | 840 | 1,040 | 2,086 | 1,531 |
| 1958 | 3,477 | 1,090 | 1,357 | 2,785 | 2,061 |

[1] For all pre-Communist sources for 22 provinces production was originally computed from yields multiplied by crop hectares. The yields in this Table 6 are computed from crop hectares (Appendix Table 4) and production (Appendix Table 5) both of which are recorded to tenths of one million. Some of these yields would be slightly different if crop hectares and production data were carried to more digits than one-tenth of one million. Therefore, in making comparisons, one should allow for the possibility of the yields per hectare being too low or too high, up to at least one per cent in some cases. For instance, the NARB Revised-M does not change yields per crop hectare from NARB Estimates-M except for the difference caused by decimal places for crop hectares and crop production.

The yields for the mainland are less than for the 22 provinces because of lower yields for Manchuria, Sikang, and Sinkiang. Production for these three areas divided by crop hectares (Appendix Table 3) indicates yields of 2,000 kg for rice, 882 kg for wheat, 1,328 kg for miscellaneous, 1,712 kg (grain-equivalent) for potatoes, and 1,318 kg for all crops. The yield for miscellaneous grains in Sikang and Sinkiang is assumed to be the same as for Manchuria. Yield of potatoes is assumed to be similar to the LU Spring Wheat Area yield for potatoes, irrigated and non-irrigated, pp. 223-226, Table 14 (see note 2B). The Manchuria yields are production divided by crop hectares.

APPENDIX TABLE 7. MOST FREQUENT YIELDS FOR VARIOUS TYPES OF RICE
ARRAYED BY GROUP INTERVALS OF 500 KILOGRAMS PER CROP HECTARE
(22 PROVINCES)[1]

| Group intervals | Number of localities | | | | |
|---|---|---|---|---|---|
| | Main crop (per one crop hectare)[1] | Glutinous rice (per one crop hectare)[1] | Double cropping (early and late rice, each as one crop hectare)[2] | Interplanted (early and late rice combined per one crop hectare)[3] | Total (for all types of rice)[4] |
| 1-499 | 0 | 0 | 0 | 0 | 0 |
| 500-999 | 0 | 0 | 0 | 0 | 0 |
| 1,000-1,499 | 3 | 1 | 3 | 0 | 7 |
| 1,500-1,999 | 5 | 2 | 5 | 0 | 12 |
| 2,000-2,499 | 11 | 7 | 2 | 0 | 20 |
| 2,500-2,999 | 20 | 3 | 1 | 0 | 24 |
| 3,000-3,499 | 10 | 1 | 2 | 4 | 17 |
| 3,500-3,999 | 8 | 3 | 2 | 0 | 13 |
| 4,000-4,499 | 2 | 2 | 0 | 1 | 5 |
| 4,500-4,999 | 4 | 1 | 1 | 0 | 6 |
| 5,000-5,499 | 1 | 0 | 0 | 1 | 2 |
| 5,500-5,999 | 2 | 0 | 0 | 0 | 2 |
| 6,000-6,499 | 3 | 0 | 0 | 0 | 3 |
| 6,500-6,999 | 1 | 0 | 0 | 0 | 1 |
| 7,000-7,499 | 0 | 0 | 0 | 0 | 0 |
| 7,500-7,999 | 0 | 0 | 0 | 0 | 0 |
| 8,000-8,499 | 1 | 0 | 0 | 0 | 1 |
| 8,500-8,999 | 1 | 0 | 0 | 0 | 1 |
| Total numbers | 72 | 20 | 16 | 6 | 114 |

[1] *LU-B,* Table 3, p. 209.
[2] *Ibid.,* Table 14, p. 223.
[3] *Ibid.,* Table 14, p. 223, and notes to Table 6, p. 198, for localities with interplanted rice.
[4] The median yield of 2,775 kg. occurs in the modal group of 2,500-2,999. It is the average of the 57th and 58th yield in the frequency distribution.

APPENDIX TABLE 8. AN ARRAY OF DENSITIES OF FARM POPULATION PER SQUARE MILE OF CROP AREA (CULTIVATED AREA) BY GROUP INTERVALS OF 100, 500 AND 1,000 PERSONS PER SQUARE MILE FOR 16,786 FARM HOUSEHOLDS, 168 LOCALITIES, 154 Hsien, 22 PROVINCES, CHINA, PAGES 423–4 (SEE NOTE 2B)

| Group intervals of 100 persons | Number of localities for | | | Group intervals of 100 persons | Number of localities for | | |
|---|---|---|---|---|---|---|---|
| | Intervals of 100 persons | Intervals of 500 persons | Intervals of 1000 persons | | Intervals of 100 persons | Intervals of 500 persons | Intervals of 1000 persons |
| 0-99 | 0 | | | 2,500 | 5 | | |
| 100 | 0 | | | 2,600 | 0 | | |
| 200 | 3 | | | 2,700 | 2 | | |
| 300 | 4 | | | 2,800 | 1 | | |
| 400 | 3 | 10 | | 2,900 | 1 | 9 | 24 |
| 500 | 7 | | | 3,000 | 2 | | |
| 600 | 6 | | | 3,100 | 0 | | |
| 700 | 12 | | | 3,200 | 3 | | |
| 800 | 10 | | | 3,300 | 0 | | |
| 900 | 15 | 50 | 60 | 3,400 | 2 | 7 | |
| 1,000 | 16 | | | 3,500 | 1 | | |
| 1,100 | 6 | | | 3,600 | 2 | | |
| 1,200 | 12 | | | 3,700 | 0 | | |
| 1,300 | 6 | | | 3,800 | 3 | | |
| 1,400 | 8 | 48 | | 3,900 | 0 | 6 | 13 |
| 1,500 | 9 | | | 4,000 | 1 | | |
| 1,600 | 3 | | | 4,100 | 0 | | |
| 1,700 | 2 | | | 4,200 | 0 | | |
| 1,800 | 2 | | | 4,300 | 1 | | |
| 1,900 | 4 | 20 | 68 | 4,400 | 0 | 2 | |
| 2,000 | 6 | | | 4,500 | 0 | | |
| 2,100 | 2 | | | 4,600 | 1 | 1 | 3 |
| 2,200 | 4 | | | | | | |
| 2,300 | 2 | | | Total localities | 168 | 168 | 168 |
| 2,400 | 1 | 15 | | | | | |

*Comment:*

The average of all densities of farm population is 1,485 persons per square mile, p. 632 Table 2, 12th col. (see note 2A) and pp. 423-24, Table 3 (see note 2B). The median of the modal group of 1,000-1,999 representing 68 localities is 1,450 persons per square mile or nearly the same as the average.

However, in the modal group of 1,000-1,999 there are 34 localities with densities of 1,000-1,299 and another 34 localities with densities of 1,300-1,999. The median of these localities is therefore 1,300 farm persons per square mile of cultivated area. This measure of density is the one used in this monograph for *LU* Farm Survey data. It eliminates any possible undue influence of the very high densities. The curve is a skew curve which would indicate that other sampling would give a similar result.

APPENDIX TABLE 9. COMPARISON OF AVAILABLE UNPROCESSED FOOD GRAINS FOR ANNUAL CONSUMPTION PER FARM CAPITA AND FOR TOTAL FARM POPULATION BY SOURCES OF DATA FOR 22 PROVINCES, CHINA

| I | LU Food Survey, 1929-33 | | NARB Food Survey, 1937 for Usual Consumption | | |
| | Average by localities[2] | Weighted average[2] | Average by localities[4] | Average by provinces[5] | Weighted average[6] |
| Food grains | II | III | IV | V | VI |
|---|---|---|---|---|---|
| **Part I. Annual per Farm Capita (in kilograms)** | | | | | |
| Total | 268.1 | 269.7 | 296.4 | 287.0 | 286.1 |
| Rice, unhulled[1] | 131.1 | 147.5 | 123.9 | 130.4 | 146.7 |
| Wheat | 35.3 | 31.3 | 40.8 | 37.2 | 33.0 |
| Miscellaneous | 91.6 | 80.9 | 122.9 | 110.0 | 97.1 |
| Potatoes (grain-equivalent) | 10.1 | 10.0 | 8.8 | 9.4 | 9.3 |
| **Part II. Annual Amount for Farm Population 441.5 million (in million metric tons)** | | | | | |
| Total | 118.4 | 119.0 | 130.9 | 126.9 | 126.4 |
| Rice, unhulled | 57.9 | 65.1 | 54.7 | 57.6 | 64.8 |
| Wheat | 15.6 | 13.8 | 18.0 | 16.4 | 14.6 |
| Miscellaneous | 40.4 | 35.7 | 54.3 | 48.7 | 42.9 |
| Potatoes (grain-equivalent) | 4.5 | 4.4 | 3.9 | 4.2 | 4.1 |

Notes on Following Page

Notes to Appendix Table 9

[1] Slightly polished rice as consumed by farmers converted to unhulled by estimated factor 0.75.

[2] This is the sum of the averages per capita for each food grain for 20 families in each of 136 localities divided by 136 (pp. 86-121, Tables 17-1 to 17-136) (see note 2B).

[3] Averages for each *LU* Agricultural Area weighted by *LU* Survey farm population of each Area, p. 362, Table 2, col. 8 (see note 2A).

[4] The NARB Food Survey in 1937 as stated in the Report (2) is for "the usual amount of consumption per person, old and young, not for any one year." The average as published (see note 5) is the average for all localities studied, i.e., totals of amounts for all localities divided by the total number of localities.

[5] For this table, the provincial averages as given in the report (see note 5) are totalled and divided by number of provinces.

[6] A correct average cannot be obtained by multiplying average provincial consumption by provincial total population because parts of several provinces are located in two or more different agricultural areas. In the absence of data by *hsien*, which if available could be arranged by agricultural areas, it is assumed that the ratio of the *LU* Food Survey average by localities, col. II, to *LU* weighted average by farm population for each of Eight Agricultural Areas, col. III, when multiplied by the NARB Food Survey average by provinces, col. V, would be the approximate equivalent of a weighted average by farm population for the NARB data if the data had been tabulated by the *LU* Eight Agricultural Areas and weighted by farm population of these areas. This method appears to give the best distribution among the four groups of food grains in relation to production as indicated in Appendix Table 10. The percentage ratios are rice, 112.5; wheat, 88.7; miscellaneous grains, 88.3 and potatoes, 99.1 per cent. These percentages are multiplied by NARB averages by provinces, col. V, to obtain weighted averages related to farm population. Mr. O. L. Dawson has kindly supplied his test computations obtained by multiplying NARB provincial averages for each food grain per farm capita by provincial populations as follows in kilograms: rice 150.7; wheat 34.6; miscellaneous 109.3; potatoes 8.2 and a total of 302.8 kg. The averages by this method for the farm groups of food grains are better than the average by localities, col. IV, or the averages by provinces, col. V, because it increases the average for rice consumption and decreases the average for miscellaneous grains and wheat, and, therefore, checks more closely with production and also with the *LU* Farm Food Survey averages weighted by farm population of each *LU* Agricultural Area in col. III. If the NARB data were arranged by *hsien* for the LU Eight Agricultural Areas the averages would probably check even more closely because a number of provinces have a portion of area in one Agricultural Area and another portion in another Agricultural Area. For instance, northern portion of Anhwei and Kiangsu provinces do not produce rice while southern portions do not produce some of the miscellaneous grains, such as green beans. Thus, both rice and green beans are over weighted for these two provinces.

APPENDIX TABLE 10. COMPARISON OF QUANTITIES OF FOOD GRAINS AVAILABLE FOR FOOD CONSUMPTION BY SOURCES OF DATA FOR FARM, NONFARM AND TOTAL POPULATION FOR 22 PROVINCES, CHINA

| Food grains | Average production (1929–33) (MMT) | Factor for food use[1] (per cent) | Available for Food | | Remainder available for non-farm population of 110.4m[3] |
|---|---|---|---|---|---|
| | | | For total population of 551.9m | For farm population of 441.5m[2] (MMT) | |
| I | II | III | IV | V | VI |
| **Part I. The *LU* Survey of Production and *LU* Food Survey, 1929–33** | | | | | |
| Total | 167.0 | 86.0 | 143.7 | 119.0 | 24.7 |
| Rice, unhulled | 87.7 | 90.7 | 79.5 | 65.1 | 14.4 |
| Wheat | 22.7 | 85.0 | 19.3 | 13.8 | 5.5 |
| Miscellaneous | 47.5 | 79.9 | 38.0 | 35.7 | 2.3 |
| Potatoes (grain equivalent) | 9.1 | 76.1 | 6.9 | 4.4 | 2.5 |
| **Part II. The NARB Revised Production, 1931–37 and the NARB Food Survey in 1937 for Usual Farm Food Consumption** | | | | | |
| Total | 155.4 | 85.4 | 132.7 | 126.4 | 6.3 |
| Rice, unhulled | 67.2 | 90.7 | 61.0 | 64.8 | −3.8 |
| Wheat | 29.1 | 85.0 | 24.7 | 14.6 | 10.1 |
| Miscellaneous | 52.3 | 79.9 | 41.8 | 42.9 | −1.1 |
| Potatoes (grain equivalent) | 6.8 | 76.1 | 5.2 | 4.1 | 1.1 |
| **Part III. Combined Estimates of Production and the *LU* Food Survey** | | | | | |
| Total | 189.2 | 84.7 | 160.3 | 119.0 | 41.3 |
| Rice, unhulled | 74.7 | 90.7 | 67.8 | 65.1 | 2.7 |
| Wheat | 29.8 | 85.0 | 25.3 | 13.8 | 11.5 |
| Miscellaneous | 72.9 | 79.9 | 58.2 | 35.7 | 22.5 |
| Potatoes (grain-equivalent) | 11.8 | 76.1 | 9.0 | 4.4 | 4.6 |

Continued on Following Page

APPENDIX TABLE 10. COMPARISON OF QUANTITIES OF FOOD GRAINS AVAILABLE FOR FOOD CONSUMPTION BY SOURCES OF DATA FOR FARM, NONFARM AND TOTAL POPULATION FOR 22 PROVINCES, CHINA

| I Food grains | II Average production (1929-33) (MMT) | III Factor for food use[1] (per cent) | Available for Food | | VI Remainder available for non-farm population of 110.4m[3] |
|---|---|---|---|---|---|
| | | | IV For total population of 551.9m | V For farm population of 441.5m[2] (MMT) | |
| Part IV. Combined Estimates Production and NARB Food Survey | | | | | |
| Total | 189.2 | 84.7 | 160.3 | 126.4 | 33.4 |
| Rice, unhulled | 74.7 | 90.7 | 67.8 | 64.8 | 3.0 |
| Wheat | 29.8 | 85.0 | 25.3 | 14.6 | 10.7 |
| Miscellaneous | 72.9 | 79.9 | 58.3 | 42.9 | 15.3 |
| Potatoes (grain-equivalent) | 11.8 | 76.1 | 9.0 | 4.1 | 4.4 |
| Part V. The NARB Revised Production, 1931-37 and LU Food Survey, 1929-33 | | | | | |
| Total | 155.4 | 85.4 | 132.7 | 119.0 | 13.7 |
| Rice, unhulled | 67.2 | 90.7 | 61.0 | 65.1 | —4.1 |
| Wheat | 29.1 | 85.0 | 24.7 | 13.8 | 10.9 |
| Miscellaneous | 52.3 | 79.9 | 41.8 | 35.7 | 6.1 |
| Potatoes (grain-equivalent) | 6.8 | 76.1 | 5.2 | 4.4 | 0.8 |

Notes to Appendix Table 10

[1] These factors for each group of grains are from Appendix Table 11, col. III. The average of these factors vary with the source of data because of differences in amounts in each group of food grains.

[2] These amounts in Parts I, III, and V are from the LU Food Survey for food grains reported by farmers weighted by population, col. III, Part II, Appendix Table 9. In Part II and IV they are from the NARB Food Survey of food consumption by farmers, col. VI, Part II, Appendix Table 9.

[3] Col. IV minus col. V. Production of potatoes for NARB Revised is lower than for the LU Survey and the remaining portion of 1.5 MMT for nonfarm population. Part II appears to be more realistic than the 2.5 MMT for LU Survey, Part I. Observation leads one to believe

that the nonfarm population does not consume as large a proportion of sweet potatoes as indicated. Although sweet potatoes are considered as the poor man's food, a considerable quantity is consumed by the nonfarm population as baked potatoes from venders in the streets of cities and towns. The *LU* Survey percentage of 76.1 of potato production available for food differs greatly from that of the FAO Balance Sheet quoted by Shen (see note 1), chiefly because of the smaller proportion of production reported as used for feed. The Balance Sheet as quoted does not indicate sources of data for the nonfood uses. It is possible that farmers underreported consumption of sweet potatoes because it is considered as the "poor man's food," although there is no clear evidence of this. The *LU* production of 9.1 is higher than NARB of 6.7 MMT but lower than Combined Crop Estimates of 11.8 MMT. At least two *LU* localities reported what appears to be too high a production, but no adjustments are made for this in the *LU* Farm Survey production data.

*Comment:*

The computations in this table are for 22 provinces rather than for mainland China because farm food consumption data are only available for 22 provinces. The *LU* Food Survey for 21 provinces did not include the province of Chahar, but since it has a small farm population its inclusion would not change the data in a significant way.

Population data from the *LU* Farm Survey (Table 5) are used in the computations for NARB Food Survey data. They are considered to be the most appropriate in the absence of any count of population for 1931-37. The use of any lower population figure would not change the production figures of each food grain available for the nonfarm population and, therefore, would not eliminate the discrepancies indicated in this table.

Some other population figure could be used, based on various methods of calculation, including backward from the 1953 Communist census. This has been done by John S. Aird in a letter to O. L. Dawson (Aird, John S., A table enclosed in a letter to O. L. Dawson dated Sept. 10, 1962, Department of Commerce, Bureau of the Census, Washington 25, D.C.). His adjustment for three different percentages of possible undercount in the 1953 census vary for his Series I for 1933 from 469.9 million to 512.1 million and for Series II for 1933 from 530.3 million to 577.9 million. Since the *LU* 592 million is based on careful sample count, as already explained, there appears to be no reason in favor of accepting a calculated population based on assumed annual increases. Aird's highest figures are undoubtedly nearer the true population than any of his other projections. Presumably the average population for 1931-37 was greater than 592 million for 1929-33 and, if so, the discrepancies between NARB Revised production and NARB Food Consumption would be even greater than indicated for the 592 million population.

If the average consumption per farm capita 286.1 kg for NARB Food Survey, as depicted in col. 6, Appendix Table 9, is accepted as the most realistic of the three averages cols. IV, V and VI, Appendix Table 9 then the increase in consumption compared with *LU* Food Survey of 269.7 kg is 6.1 per cent. The NARB production increase for 1935-37 average production portrays an increase of 103.8 per cent. The higher increase in consumption of 6.1 per cent is caused chiefly by a much higher reported consumption of miscellaneous grains relative to production for 1935-37 than for either rice, wheat, or potatoes. Wheat production actually decreased. Therefore, the 1931-37 production is used in this table for comparison with consumption because the use of 1935-37 production would not alter conclusions on discrepancies in food grains available for the nonfarm population, although the amounts remaining for nonfarm population would be somewhat different. Another reason for using the 1931-37 production is the fact that consumption was for the "most usual consumption, not for any one year," and therefore, the high production in 1936 may not have influenced reports on consumption in terms of this one year of higher consumption. Production in 1937 was only very slightly higher than the 1931-37 average.

APPENDIX TABLE 11. QUANTITIES OF FOOD GRAINS AVAILABLE FOR FOOD FROM *LU* FARM SURVEY-M AND AVAILABILITY OF CALORIES FOR FARM, NONFARM AND TOTAL POPULATION FOR MAINLAND CHINA

Part I. Annual Production and Quantities of Unprocessed Food Grains Available for Human Consumption

| | | | Available for food | | | | Remainder available for nonfarm population of 118.4m[5] (MMT) |
| | Average production[1] (1929–33) (MMT) | Factor for food use[2] (per cent) | For total population of 592m (MMT) | For farm population of 473.6m | | | |
| Food grains | | | | Per cent[3] | Amount[4] (MMT) | | |
| I | II | III | IV | V | VI | | VII |
|---|---|---|---|---|---|---|---|
| Total | 181.9 | 85.5 | 155.5 | 83.2 | 129.4 | | 26.1 |
| Rice, unhulled | 88.3 | 90.7 | 80.1 | 81.9 | 65.6 | | 14.5 |
| Wheat | 24.2 | 85.0 | 20.6 | 71.5 | 14.7 | | 5.9 |
| Miscellaneous | 58.4 | 79.9 | 46.7 | 94.0 | 43.9 | | 2.8 |
| Potatoes (grain-equivalent) | 11.0 | 76.1 | 8.1 | 63.8 | 5.2 | | 2.9 |

Part II. Annual Quantities of Unprocessed and Processed Food Grains per Capita and Calories Available

| | | | Quantities per capita after processing | | Available calories | | |
| | Annual per capita[6] (kg) | Reduction factors for processing[7] | Per year (kg) | Per day (grams) | Per kg of food grains[8] | Per capita per day[9] | From all food per capita[10] |
| Food grains | | | | | | | |
| I | II | III | IV | V | VI | VII | VIII |
|---|---|---|---|---|---|---|---|
| A. For farm population of 473.6m | | | | | | | |
| Total | 273.2 | .806 | 220.2 | 603.4 | 3,528 | 2,129 | 2,425 |
| Rice, unhulled | 138.5 | .75 | 103.9 | 284.6 | 3,521 | 1,002 | |
| Wheat | 31.0 | .86 | 26.7 | 73.2 | 3,485 | 255 | |
| Miscellaneous | 92.7 | .86 | 79.7 | 218.5 | 3,624 | 791 | |
| Potatoes (grain equivalent) | 11.0 | .90 | 9.9 | 27.1 | 2,973 | 81 | |

| | | | | | | |
|---|---|---|---|---|---|---|
| **B. For nonfarm population of 118.4m** | | | | | | |
| Total | 220.4 | .761 | 460.1 | 167.8 | 3,460 | 1,592 | 2,123 or 2,349 with imports |
| Rice, unhulled | 122.5 | .70 | 235.0 | 85.6 | 3,521 | 827 | |
| Wheat | 49.8 | .80 | 109.0 | 39.8 | 3,520 | 384 | |
| Miscellaneous | 23.6 | .86 | 55.6 | 20.3 | 3,624 | 201 | |
| Potatoes (grain equivalent) | 24.5 | .90 | 60.5 | 22.1 | 2,973 | 180 | |
| **C. For total population of 592m** | | | | | | |
| Total | 261.8 | .801 | 574.7 | 209.8 | 3,520 | 2,023 | 2,365 or 2,410 with imports |
| Rice, unhulled | 135.3 | .74 | 274.2 | 100.1 | 3,521 | 965 | |
| Wheat | 34.8 | .848 | 80.8 | 29.5 | 3,492 | 282 | |
| Miscellaneous | 78.9 | .86 | 186.0 | 67.9 | 3,624 | 674 | |
| Potatoes (grain-equivalent) | 13.7 | .90 | 33.7 | 12.3 | 2,972 | 102 | |

[1] Production data are from col. VI Appendix Table 5.

[2] These factors are computed from utilization of food grains on farms p. 236, Table 23 (See Note 2B) and other used for quantities marketed p. 82, Table 12 (See Note 15 *Professional Manpower and Education in Communist China*) plus losses at five per cent of production. The average of these factors of 85.5 per cent is higher than the computed weighted average of 82.0 per cent for losses and other nonfarm food uses in the FAO Food Balance Sheet for the 22 provinces, p. 378, Appendix Table 4 (See Note 1). Losses are computed at a higher amount than in the FAO Food Balance Sheet. Sample losses in storage alone for six provinces indicate an average loss of 12 per cent, p. 48 (II). The lower percentage of food in the FAO Balance Sheet appears to be caused in part by the exclusion of food grains used for wine or liquor and to the use of a proportion for feed and seed applicable only to annual of production used on farm rather than to the total production.

[3] These percentages for 22 provinces are obtained by dividing *LU* survey food grains available for farm population, col. V, Appendix Table 10 by the total food grains available for total population col. IV, Appendix Table 10. It is assumed that these percentages also represent the approximate proportion of food grains available for farm consumption for mainland China which includes Manchuria, Sikang and Sinkiang in addition to the 22 provinces.

[4] Col. IV x col. V.

[5] Col. IV minus col. VI.

[6] Col. VI, Part I divided by 473.6 million farm population (Table 5).

[7] No exact comprehensive information is available on the proportion of edible food available after processing food grains. In the *LU* Food Consumption study, rice was reported in the form of "mi". The term "mi" is a general one for rice after the hulls are removed and for various degrees of milling and polishing. Since farmers, in general, consume lightly milled rice, it is assumed that the rice reported had 75 per cent of hulls plus bran removed from unhulled or paddy rice. For nonfarm population a factor of 70 per cent of unhulled rice is used for available rice after processing. A partial clue to processing is indicated in Table 16—A, B C, E and F, p. 85 (See Note 2B), but this applies only to grain that is

Notes to Table 11 (*Continued on following page*)

Notes to Table 11

processed. Considerable quantities of whole grain are used by farmers either as flour or congee. The average of the data on processing for wheat, kaoliang, corn, barley and green beans (mung) into flour in regions where the product is a major one is 84.9 per cent. In the absence of a more precise indication, it is assumed that at least 86 per cent is used for wheat and also for miscellaneous grains consumed by farmers. For nonfarm population 80 per cent is used for wheat but 86 per cent for miscellaneous grains which are chiefly consumed by laboring classes of nonfarm population. For potatoes 90 per cent potatoes is considered available after peeling.

[8] The calories in this column are based on the chemical composition and caloric value of food products p. 67, Table 2 (See Note 2B). Dr. Leonard A. Maynard, an authority on nutrition and co-author of the chapter on nutrition, in a letter to J. L. Buck dated May 18, 1962, has explained that "These caloric values were calculated from Sherman's Table (Buck, John Lossing, Director, The 1931 Flood in China—An Economic Survey, University of Nanking in Cooperation with the National Flood Relief Commission, April 1932, pp 74.) and a Chinese table which used Atwater's General Factors: protein 4; fat 9; and carbohydrates 4, which he set up for the average American diet. It would have been more exact if we had used other factors more applicable to a largely vegetarian diet . . . I'm not sure that the figures would be changed essentially. The use of specific factors instead of general factors is illustrated by the data in the USDA Yearbook No. 8 which is now our guide for food consumption." Dr. Maynard has discussed this problem of caloric value of diets in connection with the importance of achieving uniformity for comparisons of caloric values of diets of different countries (See Note 13).

The caloric values in Table 2, p. 67 (See Note 2B) are for edible portions of the whole grain unprocessed except for rice which, as consumed by farmers, is lightly milled after removal of hulls. The available calories per kilogram for each group of food grains in this col. VI are obtained by weighting calories for each product in Table 2, p. 67 (See Note 2B) by amount of each food grain.

[9] These computations for cols. VII and VIII do not represent actual caloric intake because of possible losses, including losses in preparation of food. Also the caloric values may be somewhat different for the Chinese diet which is largely vegetarian, and especially so for the farm population. The extent to which these amounts of calories are actually available depends also upon the factors used for proportion of production available and on the proportion of food available after processing.

[10] Calories available from all food for the farm population are obtained by dividing 2,129 calories from food grains by 87.8 per cent, the LU Survey proportion of calories from all food, p. 413, Table 6 (See Note 2A). For nonfarm population a factor of 75 per cent of all food calories is assumed to be from food grains, although the actual factor for all segments of nonfarm population may be different. Dietary Surveys, 1937-39, of Public Works Employees, Shanghai (Hou, D. H. C.: Mar, P. C.: Read, B. E., Dietary Surveys, 1937-39, of Public Works Employees Shanghai, Henry Lester Institute of Medical Research, Shanghai.) indicate 70 per cent from food grains, excluding grain-equivalent of potatoes.

If the imports (1929-33) of rice in terms of unhulled rice of 1.4 MMT and wheat and wheat flour in terms of wheat of 1.1 MMT are assumed to be consumed chiefly by the nonfarm population the calories from food grains would increase from 1,592 to 1,762 calories and the total calories for all food from 2,123 to 2,349 calories. This would increase the 2,365 calories for total population to 2,410 calories. These amounts of calories, as already mentioned, do not indicate the actual caloric intake because of losses and possibly because of a different metabolism for a vegetarian diet.

APPENDIX TABLE 12. COMMUNIST QUANTITIES OF FOOD GRAINS AVAILABLE FOR FOOD AND AVAILABILITY OF CALORIES FOR FARM, NONFARM AND TOTAL POPULATION FOR MAINLAND CHINA, 1949–58

Part I. Annual Production and Quantities of Unprocessed Food Grains Available for Human Consumption

| | Average production[1] (1929–33) (MMT) | Factor for food use[2] (per cent) | Available for food | | | Remainder available for nonfarm population of 119.4m[5] (MMT) |
| | | | For total population of 596.8m (MMT) | For farm population of 477.4 m | | |
| Food grains | | | | Per cent[3] | Amount[4] (MMT) | |
| I | II | III | IV | V | VI | VII |
| Total | 163.2 | .845 | 137.9 | 82.0 | 113.1 | 24.8 |
| Rice, unhulled | 73.8 | .907 | 66.1 | 81.9 | 54.1 | 12.0 |
| Wheat | 20.6 | .850 | 17.5 | 71.5 | 12.5 | 5.0 |
| Miscellaneous | 49.4 | .799 | 39.5 | 94.0 | 37.1 | 2.4 |
| Potatoes (grain-equivalent) | 19.4 | .761 | 14.8 | 63.8 | 9.4 | 5.4 |

Part II. Annual Quantities of Unprocessed and Processed Food Grains Per Capita and Calories Available

| | Annual unprocessed per capita[6] (kg) | Reduction factors for processing[7] | Quantities per capita after processing | | Available calories | | |
| | | | Per year (kg) | Per day (grams) | Per kg of food grains[8] | Per capita per day[9] | From all food per capita[10] |
| Food grains | | | | | | | |
| I | II | III | IV | V | VI | VII | VIII |
| A. Farm population of 477.4m | | | | | | | |
| Total | 236.9 | .81 | 192.0 | 526.0 | 3,530 | 1,842 | 2,098 |
| Rice, unhulled | 113.3 | .75 | 85.0 | 232.9 | 3,521 | 820 | |
| Wheat | 26.2 | .86 | 22.5 | 61.6 | 3,485 | 215 | |
| Miscellaneous | 77.7 | .86 | 66.8 | 183.0 | 3,624 | 663 | |
| Potatoes (grain-equivalent) | 19.7 | .90 | 17.7 | 48.5 | 2,973 | 144 | |

Continued on Following Page

APPENDIX TABLE 12. COMMUNIST QUANTITIES OF FOOD GRAINS AVAILABLE FOR FOOD AND AVAILABILITY OF CALORIES FOR FARM, NONFARM AND TOTAL POPULATION FOR MAINLAND CHINA, 1949–58—(Continued)

Part II. Annual Quantities of Unprocessed and Processed Food Grains Per Capita and Calories Available—(Continued)

| Food grains | Annual unprocessed per capita[6] (kg) | Reduction factors for processing[7] | Quantities per capita after processing | | Per kg of food grains[8] | Available calories | From all food per capita[10] |
| | | | Per year (kg) | Per day (grams) | | Per capita per day[9] | |
| I | II | III | IV | V | VI | VII | VIII |
| B. Nonfarm population of 119.4m | | | | | | | |
| Total | 207.7 | .779 | 161.9 | 443.6 | 3,532 | 1,499 | 1,999 |
| Rice, unhulled | 100.5 | .70 | 70.4 | 192.9 | 3,521 | 679 | |
| Wheat | 41.9 | .80 | 33.5 | 91.8 | 3,520 | 317 | |
| Miscellaneous | 20.1 | .86 | 17.3 | 47.4 | 3,624 | 172 | |
| Potatoes (grain-equivalent) | 45.2 | .90 | 40.7 | 111.5 | 2,973 | 331 | |
| C. Total population of 596.8m | | | | | | | |
| Total | 231.0 | .805 | 185.9 | 509.3 | 3,487 | 1,776 | 2,078 or 2,017 minus exports |
| Rice, unhulled | 110.7 | .74 | 81.9 | 224.4 | 3,521 | 790 | |
| Wheat | 29.3 | .848 | 24.8 | 67.9 | 3,520 | 239 | |
| Miscellaneous | 66.2 | .86 | 56.9 | 155.9 | 3,624 | 565 | |
| Potatoes (grain-equivalent) | 24.8 | .90 | 22.3 | 61.1 | 2,973 | 182 | |

[1] Production data are from col. VI, Appendix Table 5.

[2] These factors are the same as in Appendix Table 11, col. III as described in note 2. Because of a greater amount of public storage of grains by the Communists it is probable that the factor for losses would be greater than for 1929-33. See note 7 to Appendix Table 11 for discussion of processing. Processing under the Communist regime may have been less refined.

[3] These percentages for the four groups of food grains are the same as those in col. V, Appendix Table 11.

[4] Col. IX × col. V.

[5] Col. IV minus col. VI.

[6] For farm population col. VI, Part I divided by 477.4 million. For nonfarm population col. VII, Part I divided by 119.4 million.

[7] For farm population the same factors as for col. III, Part II Appendix Table 11. For nonfarm population the same factors as for col. III, Part II B, Appendix Table 11.

[8] See note 8, Appendix Table 11.

[9] See note 9, Appendix Table 11.

[10] See note 10, Appendix Table 11, except the paragraph on imports. Exports by the Communists 1949-58 according to Dr. Y. L. Wu's Table 1, averages 0.9 MMT. For the average year-end total population of 596.8 million this represents a decrease of —61 calories from 2,078 calories to 2,017 calories which is 83.7 per cent of LU Food Survey-M plus imports of 2,410 calories for total population. If accumulation of stocks were above year to year requirements the amount of calories available would be less than 2,045.

YUAN-LI WU

# The Economics of Mainland China's Agriculture: Some Aspects of Measurement, Interpretation and Evaluation

## I. PRODUCTION VERSUS DISTRIBUTION—THE CRUX OF THE CHINESE AGRICULTURAL PROBLEM

On the question, how to increase agricultural production and the farmer's income, opinion was divided in pre-Communist China. One school of thought placed the principal emphasis on increase in production per unit area and per man which, according to studies of farm operation, was considered a function of size of business (not only size of farm). An increase in effective labor and capital inputs increases the size of business. The vegetable gardener with a farm one-tenth the size of that of a grain farmer has a farm business as large as, or larger than, the latter. Moreover, for a farm of the same size, an owner farmer has a larger farm business than a tenant farmer, because he supplies more capital than the tenant farmer. Thus, conversion of tenant farms into owner farms increases size of business for the former tenant by increasing his investment.

The possible expansion of the average size of the farm for all China is more problematic than increases in production

73

per unit area because of the low land-man ratio. Settlement of new areas in China under the traditional system of farming has resulted in a similar low land-man ratio. An increase in off-farm employment opportunities might increase size of farm to the extent that whole families would move away and the land would be sold or rented to other farmers. An increase in nonfarm activities on the spot would have the same effect without necessitating a physical transfer of the farmers. In cases where only a portion of the family members left the farm, the use of improved implements would make it possible for fewer people to farm the same amount of land as before, thus increasing farm income per man but not changing size of farm.*

It was recognized that mass poverty could be alleviated only through increase in size of business—provided, of course, that the beneficial effect would not be offset by increase in the unequal distribution of farm income through usurious interest and higher land rents.

Others in pre-Communist China were more concerned with the distributive aspect of farm income. Theoretical support of their position could also be found in the argument that high land rent and usury would preclude borrowing for investment purposes. Instead, they would lead to "waste" of the savings of land owners in the form of consumption loans, and, because of the inability of the poor farmers to meet their obligations, to the increasing concentration of land ownership in fewer and fewer hands. Consequently, the first step toward the solution of China's agrarian problem would have to be the redistribution of land or "land reform." Rent and interest controls would, of course, be preliminary to redistribution.

That industrialization, interpreted here broadly as the development of alternative forms of nonagricultural em-

---

* According to Irene Tauber, the farm population in Japan did not decrease in numbers, except possibly temporarily, although the proportion of farm population to total population did decrease.

ployment, constitutes the fundamental solution of China's agrarian problem cannot be denied, for the limited land available constitutes a real constraint to agricultural expansion. In spite of varying estimates of the amount of arable land in mainland China, none has put it at more than 20 per cent of the total land area, some at considerably less. The highest estimate of cultivated land in *Land Utilization in China* [1] was 108.2 million hectares, while the highest claim under the Communists was 112 million hectares in 1956. The economic feasibility of increasing the cultivated area and the speed at which this can be done are both subject to serious doubt. The question, then, is how to expand the size of the farm as an operating unit if not much new land can be brought under cultivation. One alternative would be to allow the more efficient farmers to expand their scale of operation and to have the displaced farmers absorbed into other forms of employment. A second alternative would be to merge the individual farms into cooperatives, leaving the surplus farmers alone in a state of underemployment or, as in the first case, absorbing them into other forms of employment. In each case, of course, in order to avoid undesirable political and social consequences, there would be the problem of regulating the speed at which surplus farm labor would be separated from farming, and of matching this release of labor with an appropriate rate of absorption into other employments.

The Communist party of China adopted the solution of collectivization as a means of increasing the size of the operating farm unit, because it was, and still is, ideologically opposed to the emergence of a "rich peasant" economy. However, for political reasons, it went about collectivization in a roundabout manner by first advocating and then carrying out a land redistribution program. The advocacy of land

[1] John Lossing Buck, *Land Utilization in China* (Chicago: University of Chicago Press, 1937 [out of print]; Nanking, China: University of Nanking, 1937 [out of print]).

reform earned for the Communists the reputation of being agrarian reformers, which was exceedingly helpful in foreign as well as domestic propaganda. The implementation of the land reform program, carried out in most parts of the country during 1950–52, was instrumental in redistributing wealth and both political and economic power in rural areas. The process of collectivization or formation of cooperatives was spearheaded by the formation of "mutual aid" teams, and was carried out mostly in 1954–56. In 1958, the cooperative farms were further merged into communes, although the operating unit was the "production brigade," which corresponded to the cooperative farm in size.

## Some Unresolved Questions

How effective has the Communist solution been? Has production increased with the successive institutional changes? If this has not always been what other underlying reasons can account for the institutional changes undertaken, apart from the political consideration which prompted the initial "land reform"? In particular, what accounted for the transition from the cooperative farm to the commune? What technical factors have affected the course of development of agricultural output? What conditions would seem to be necessary for the recovery and expansion of agricultural output in the light of the experience of the first decade and a half of Communist rule, particularly of the period since 1958?

## II. THE NEED FOR A REAPPRAISAL OF OFFICIAL COMMUNIST STATISTICS

Before one can evaluate the accomplishments of Communist China in the agricultural sector, an attempt must be made to determine certain quantitative records. In this connection, if the official series of the gross value of agricultural output were used, an annual rate of increase of 4.5 per cent would be indicated during the First Five-Year Plan. However, this claim is subject to dispute. The principal point at issue lies in the questionable output statistics of major subsectors in agriculture. In particular, attention should be focused on the official food grain output estimates.

The strong possibility that Communist China's food grain production statistics may be highly unreliable was first brought to sharp focus in 1958–59. Grain production in 1958 was initially reported in 1958 and early 1959 at 375 million metric tons as against 185 million tons in 1957. The alleged doubling of grain output in one year was seen by some western observers as virtually impossible, although it was generally agreed that a considerable increase in production could be brought about over a period of time. This official claim was subsequently reduced rather sharply to 250 million tons in August 1959.[2] A reduction as large as one-third of the original estimate attributed to statistical inexperience of the reporting personnel cast rather serious doubt on the accuracy of the entire statistical series, including both the revised estimate for 1958 and the reports of earlier years.

A number of reasons can be advanced to explain the unreliability of Communist China's grain statistics and to offer possible avenues of their adjustment. The several possible sources of error may be outlined as follows: (1) For the year 1958, the discrepancy between the original estimate and the revised estimate released in 1959 may be accounted for by a confusion in the estimate of unit area yield and inconsistency between the yield estimate and the acreage estimate employed in arriving at the total output. (2) A second source of error contained in grain output statistics before 1958 may consist of the underestimate of planted acreage in the earlier years. (3) For the period from 1958 on, especially in 1958–62, an overestimate of grain production may occur because of the unusually large discrepancy between "bio-

[2] Reported in the *Wall Street Journal*, Aug. 27, 1959.

logical yield" and "barn yield," due to the inability of the
communes to harvest all the crops and a sharp increase in
wastage.

Depending upon how the adjustments are made, the revised grain output statistics would differ considerably from
the official output data. The result of one series of such
adjustments is presented in Tables 1 and 2. As a consequence
of the adjustments, the rate of growth of grain production
during the period prior to the sharp decline which began in
1959 would be reduced to below the official claim. If the
adjusted estimates are correct, it would follow that the long-
term trend of grain production in mainland China is quite
modest. Inasmuch as the trend, based on the adjusted estimates for 1950–57, spanned a period during which there was
little technological change in the agricultural sector, one
may take the trend as representative of what can be nor-
mally expected of grain production given only some gradual
improvements in agricultural technology. It follows further
that should such a long-term trend fail to meet the grain
requirements of an increasing population determined on an
autarkic basis, the estimated deficiency would have to be
met through technological changes not previously allowed
for in the derivation of the trend. A methodology may then
be developed to evaluate the future prospect of Chinese
agriculture and its principal determinants.

## III. THE YIELD AND ACREAGE ESTIMATES

The source of the statistical error which gave rise to the
large overestimate of the 1958 crop was first suggested in a
1958 article by Wang Kuang-sheng in *Statistical Research*.[3]
The same explanation was pointed out by the present author
at a meeting of the Association for Asian Studies in 1960.[4]

[3] *T'ung-chi Yen-chiu* (Statistical Research) (Peking), No. 1 (Jan. 1958),
pp. 33–38.

[4] Yuan-li Wu (Walter Froehlich, ed.), *Land Tenure, Industrialization, and
Social Stability: Experience and Prospeet in Asia* (Milwaukee: Marquette
University Press, 1961).

According to Wang, the standard method adopted by the Statistical Bureau in 1956 for computing unit area yield for food grain is as follows: (1) Aggregate of area planted (excluding land for green manure) ÷ total cultivated area = the general index of multiple cropping. (2) Aggregate of area planted to grain (i.e., the crop hectare area) ÷ the general index of multiple cropping = area of cultivated land taken up by grain (i.e., the crop area under grain). (3) Total output of grain ÷ the area of cultivated land taken up by grain = the average yield of grain per unit area. In other words, the average yield of grain corresponds to yield per unit-crop area; it is not yield per crop hectare. This means that the yield per unit of crop area would be higher than the yield per crop hectare since the crop hectares in food grains are greater than the crop area in grains. In estimating the total grain output on the basis of sample-unit-area yield (i.e., yield per unit crop area under grain) , one should of course multiply the unit area yield by the crop area under grain. If by any chance one were to multiply the yield per hectare of crop area by the number of crop hectares planted, the estimate would exceed the correct total by a factor equal to the multiple cropping index. Furthermore, any extention of double cropping of any crop would increase the general multiple cropping index and correspondingly raise the unit area yield of grain.

Notwithstanding Wang Kuang-sheng's discussion, the official *Handbook of Agricultural Statistical Work* issued in 1956 stated that various types of yields could be compiled on the basis of sown acreage, harvested acreage, and cultivated acreage for different categories of crops. Furthermore, for agricultural planning, the instruction was to compute yields on the basis of sown acreage although whether output was to be the actual harvest or the expected harvest was not clear. Finally, actual practice tends to lag behind the official instructions. Thus, there may be a considerable difference between any two of the following concepts, namely, the actual harvested yield per hectare sown, the expected yield before harvest per hectare sown, and the expected yield before harvest per hectare cultivated (or harvested). Whatever may be the concept of yield employed, if it is based on a sample, and if the sample is biased in favor of high yield farms—perhaps small experimental plots—there would be an added source of upward bias.

In the case of the 1958 initial estimate of 375 million tons, the corresponding unit area yield reported at the time was a rounded figure of 3 tons per hectare. If we take this unit area estimate as yield per hectare of crop area and divide it by the general multiple cropping index of 1.45 reported for 1958, the unit yield per crop hectare would be approximately 2,070 kilograms. If this figure is then multiplied by the 1958 grain hectare area reported in 1959, or 121 million hectares, the estimated output would be equal to approximately 250 million tons. This was precisely the revised figure reported in 1959.

The preceding operation would seem to substantiate the hypothesis that the initial official claim of 1958 erred in the application of the formula for computing the grain yield. That such an error could take place can only be explained by the dilution of the statistical staff in the Bureau and its field offices, and by the insistence of the Communist party to allow politics to "take command" even in such matters as the reporting of statistics.

## IV. UNDERESTIMATE OF GRAIN OUTPUT STATISTICS BEFORE 1958

Turning next to the pre-1958 output estimate, there is reason to believe that the earlier figures underestimated actual output. This hypothesis is based on the view that if consumption estimates were made for the years 1950–56, withdrawals from stock during 1950–56 would reach a cumu-

TABLE 1. FOOD BALANCE SHEET BASED ON OFFICIAL PRODUCTION STATISTICS
(MILLION METRIC TONS)

| Year of Consumption | Production of Cereals and Potatoes in Preceding Year (in grain-equivalent) (1) | Accumulated Stock (2) | Waste (3) | Seeds (4) | Feed (5) | Manufacture (6) | Net Export (7) | Total Available for Human Consumption and Stock (8)=[(1)+(2)]−[(3)+(4)+(5)+(6)+(7)] |
|---|---|---|---|---|---|---|---|---|
| 1950 | 108.1 | ... | 3.9 | 5.6 | 8.6 | 2.9 | -- | 87.1 |
| 1951 | 124.7 | ... | 4.6 | 6.4 | 10.4 | 3.8 | -- | 99.5 |
| 1952 | 135.1 | ... | 5.0 | 6.9 | 10.8 | 4.0 | +0.9 | 107.5 |
| 1953 | 154.4 | 6.3* | 5.8 | 7.9 | 12.9 | 4.7 | +0.9 | 122.2 |
| 1954 | 156.9 | 9.5* | 5.9 | 8.0 | 12.8 | 4.7 | +1.1 | 130.7 |
| 1955 | 160.5 | 16.0* | 6.0 | 8.4 | 12.6 | 4.7 | +1.3 | 137.0 |
| 1956 | 174.8 | 15.5* | 6.6 | 9.0 | 14.0 | 5.2 | +1.2 | 154.8 |
| 1957 | 182.5 | 22.9* | 7.0 | 9.5 | 14.3 | 5.3 | +1.1 | 160.8 |
| 1958 | 185.0 | 32.9* | 7.1 | 9.5 | 14.3 | 5.3 | +1.2 | 170.5 |
| 1959 | 250.0 | 89.2 | 10.7 | 12.9 | 20.6 | 7.4 | +1.7 | 229.6 |
| 1960 | 220.0* | 155.7 | 9.4 | 11.4 | 18.1 | 6.5 | --- | 263.8 |
| 1961 | 185.0† | | 7.9 | 9.6 | 15.2 | 5.5 | −5.6 | 308.1 |

Throughout this monograph ... indicates no information --- indicates nil
* Unadjusted estimates based on official sources
† Government stock only

TABLE 1. (CONT'D) FOOD BALANCE SHEET BASED ON OFFICIAL PRODUCTION STATISTICS (MILLION METRIC TONS)

| Year of Consumption | Estimated Human Consumption (9) | Net Remaining as Stock (10)=(8)−(9) (Possibly fictitious) | Net Remaining for Additional Stock at End of Year (11)=(10)−(2) |
|---|---|---|---|
| 1950 | 133.9 | −46.8 | −46.8 |
| 1951 | 136.6 | −37.1 | −37.1 |
| 1952 | 139.3 | −31.8 | −31.8 |
| 1953 | 142.4 | −20.2 | −20.2 |
| 1954 | 145.7 | −15.0 | −21.3 |
| 1955 | 148.9 | −11.9 | −21.4 |
| 1956 | 152.1 | +2.7 | −13.3 |
| 1957 | 141.8 | +19.0 | +3.5 |
| 1958 | 160.2 | +10.3 | −12.6 |
| 1959 | 140.4 | +89.2 | +56.3 |
| 1960 | 108.1 | +155.7 | +66.5 |
| 1961 | 101.1 | +207.0 | +51.3 |

## Notes to Table 1.

Col. 1: Source: *Wei-ta ti Shih-nien* (Great Ten Years), Peking, 1959, p. 105.

Col. 2: Government cumulative stock plus non-government cumulative stock. For 1953-56, the former is given in *T'ung-chi Kung-tso* (Statistical Work), No. 19, 1957, p. 32.

Col. 3: 3 per cent of gross output of paddy rice, wheat and other cereals; 10 per cent of gross output of tubers, T. H. Shen, *China's Agricultural Resources*, Appendix, Ithaca, New York, 1951.

Col. 4: Paddy rice, 2.9 per cent of gross; wheat, 9.5 per cent; other cereals, 6 per cent; tubers, 6.9 per cent. These are weighted means derived from the 1931-37 data for 22 provinces and 1937-38 data for Manchuria given by Shen, *op. cit.*

Col. 5: 1 per cent of gross wheat output; 18.5 per cent of miscellaneous cereals; 19.4 per cent of tubers; none for rice. Columns 5 and 6 are both derived from Shen, *op. cit.*

Col. 6: Paddy rice, 1 per cent of gross production; wheat, 2 per cent; other cereals, 5.5 per cent; tubers, 5 per cent.

Col. 7: Estimated as follows: 1953-56, derived from *T'ung-chi Kung-tso*, 1957 (see reference under column 2); 1958-59, *Tsu-kuo* (China Weekly), No. 423, pp. 3-4, Hong Kong, 1961; 1952, same as 1953; 1957, average of 1953-56; 1961-62, derived from *Far Eastern Economic Review*, Vol. XXXIV, No. 2, Hong Kong, October 21, 1961, p. 128.

Col. 9: Unit consumption of unprocessed grain (kg. per adult per year) × adult equivalent population at midyear (millions) ÷ 1000 = total consumption of unprocessed grain in M. T.

1950-56: In 1955 rationing regulations were promulgated by Communist China. The ration amounted to 201 kg. a year for a person doing light work in rice-eating and wheat-flour-eating regions. The corresponding ratios for a person doing heavy work was 252 kg. per year. Weighted in accordance with the 1954-56 urban (14 per cent) and rural (86 per cent) population respectively, the national mean grain consumption per adult would work out at 245 kg. of processed grain.

1957: 210 kg. of processed grain per adult per year.

1958: Same as 1950-56 period, 245 kg.

1959: 202 kg. per adult per year.

1960: 150 kg. per adult per year.

1961: 145 kg. per adult per year.

1962: 145 kg. per adult per year.

Unit consumption of processed grain ÷ 0.86 (milling factor) = unit consumption of unprocessed grain (except for 1957, 1959, and 1960 due to slight differences in the grain mix).

Adult equivalent population = total midyear population × 0.86 (conversion factor derived from age composition given in *Jen-min Pao-chien* (People's Health) Vol. 1, No. 5, p. 463, Peking, May 1959). Through 1957 the data are based on official estimates. For 1958-59 the estimates are based on an annual growth of 2.2 per cent. The 1960-62 estimates are at a slightly lower rate of increase. The original data of midyear total population in millions are:

1950, 547; 1951, 558; 1952, 569; 1953, 581; 1954, 595; 1955, 608; 1956, 621; 1957, 637; 1958, 654; 1959, 668; 1960, 682; 1961, 693; 1962, 702; 1963, 711.

Sources: "Chukoku no Shokuryo Jijo," *Ajia Keizai Jumpo* (Asian Economic Thrice-Monthly), No. 450, pp. 1-10, Tokyo, November 20, 1960; *Shih-shih Shou-ts'e* (Current Events), No. 15, Peking, 1957, p. 18; additional sources cited in the author's article "Farm Crisis in Red China," *Current History*, September 1959, p. 192.

lative total of nearly 200 million tons. Furthermore, there was a minimum of 15.5 million tons of government stock at the end of 1956. The initial stock in 1950 could not possibly have approached such a phenomenal volume. Inasmuch as food was not rationed at the beginning of the 1950's, and inasmuch as the consumption estimates used in this hypothetical food balance sheet (Table 1) would yield a per capita calorie intake (about 2,350 calories per adult per day) below the level of the normal prewar diet, it would seem that the computed heavy withdrawal of stock was, in fact, a fictitious one. In other words, there must have been a serious underestimate of current production. Allowing for such uses as animal feed, seed requirements, and raw material in manufacturing, plus some waste in processing, the underestimate of net supply of food grain available for human consumption during the year must be raised by approximately 25 per cent to arrive at the underestimate of gross output.

According to official statistics, the area of cultivated land in Communist China increased steadily from 100.4 million hectares in 1950 to 112 million hectares in 1956. The mean for 1955–57 would amount to 111.2 million hectares which happens to correspond fairly closely to Buck's highest estimate in *Land Utilization in China*, combined with estimates for Manchuria, Jehol, Sinkiang, and Sikang or 108.8 million hectares. It is somewhat higher than the official estimate of 107.8 million hectares for 1958, which, though seemingly plausible, we have chosen to disregard because of the general unreliability of statistics of that year. Parallel to the rising trend of cultivated land, the crop hectare area planted to cereals and potatoes rose in official statistics from 104.8 million hectares in 1950 to 124.3 million hectares in 1956. The mean for 1955–57 is 121.2 million hectares. A hypothesis can, therefore, be advanced to the effect that the reported increase in cultivated land, as well as in hectares planted, up to 1956 was essentially a statistical increase due to better reporting coverage. That 1956 should be the terminal year for this statistical phenomenon would not be surprising in view of the fact that the program of collectivization was completed in 1956 and that land statistics probably became more accurate in that year. Of course, one may raise the question why the land statistics had not been better in the earlier years in view of the land reform program carried out in 1950–53. The explanation may lie in the fact that the State Statistical Bureau was not established until the end of 1952; furthermore, the statistical reporting system, especially in the rural areas, was not fully established and the returns were not standardized until several years later. Table 2 presents a possible model of adjustment on this basis.

## V. OVERESTIMATE OF GRAIN OUTPUT STATISTICS IN 1958–60

It is generally known that the curtailment of personal consumption of the staple foods began in 1959 and that it became quite serious in 1960–62. It is also common knowledge that Communist China's policy of autarky in grain supply was reversed for the first time in 1961, and grain imports have continued up to this writing (1964). Consequently, one would assume that the existence of any sizeable stock at the end of 1961 may be safely precluded. Yet, if the grain output statistics in Table 1 were employed for the years 1958–60, there would emerge a cumulative addition to stock between 1957 and 1961 equivalent to some 165 million tons. This inconsistency implies that an overestimate of production still existed in the revised official claims. As an approximation, this overestimate can be taken out of the data for 1958–60, this adjustment is made in Table 2. The result is a discount of 38 per cent for 1958 and a minimum discount of 28 per cent for 1960.

TABLE 2. AN ADJUSTED MODEL FOOD BALANCE SHEET
(MILLION METRIC TONS)

| Year of Consumption | Adjusted Production of Cereals and Potatoes in Preceding Year (1) | Estimated Production Deducted from Waste, Seed, Feed, and Mfg. (1)×0.8=(2) | Net Export (3) | Total Available for Human Consumption and Stock (4)=(2)−(3) | Estimated Human Consumption (5) | Net Remaining for Addition to Stock (6)=(4)−(5) | Cumulative Amount of Col. (6) (Exclusive of Initial Stock at 1950 Year End) |
|---|---|---|---|---|---|---|---|
| 1951 | 179.8 | 143.8 | --- | 143.8 | 136.6 | +7.2 | +7.2 |
| 1952 | 182.9 | 146.3 | +0.9 | 145.4 | 139.3 | +6.1 | +13.3 |
| 1953 | 184.2 | 147.4 | +0.9 | 146.5 | 142.4 | +4.1 | +17.4 |
| 1954 | 180.0 | 144.0 | +1.1 | 142.9 | 145.7 | −2.8 | +14.6 |
| 1955 | 177.1 | 141.7 | +1.3 | 140.4 | 148.9 | −8.5 | +6.1 |
| 1956 | 184.1 | 147.3 | +1.2 | 146.1 | 152.1 | −6.0 | +0.1 |
| 1957 | 182.5 | 146.0 | +1.1 | 144.9 | 141.8 | +3.1 | +3.2 |
| 1958 | 185.0 | 148.0 | +1.2 | 146.8 | 160.2 | −13.4 | −10.2 |
| 1959 | 175.4 | 140.3 | +1.7 | 138.6 | 140.4 | −1.8 | −12.0 |
| 1960 | 154.4 | 123.5 | --- | 123.5 | 108.1 | +15.4 | +3.4 |
| 1961 | 130.0 | 104.0 | −5.6 | 109.6 | 101.1 | +8.5 | +11.9 |
| 1962 | 140.0 | 112.0 | −3.2 | 115.2 | 103.5 | +11.7 | +23.6 |
| 1963 | 160.0 | 128.0 | −4.7 | 132.7 | (a)113.0<br>(b)143.6 | +19.7<br>−10.9 | +43.3<br>−12.7 |

Column (1): 1950-55.—The cumulative total of withdrawals from stock in 1950-56 in Table 1 amounted to 191.9 million tons (Table 1, col. 11). At the end of 1956 the minimum value of government stock was 15.5 million tons. However, the initial stock in 1950 could not possibly approach the total of these two figures—about 208 million tons. To allow for any possible overestimate of consumption as well as for the initial stock at the beginning of 1950, we disregard the 46.8 million tons in 1950 and assume the cumulative total of withdrawals in 1951-56 to be 145.1 million tons. The last figure is treated as a reflection of the total extent of underestimation of net supply derived from the production of 1950-55. 145.1 million tops plus 20 per cent of the gross output alloted to seeds, feed, waste, and manufacturing, leads to a total underestimate of about nearly 181.8 million metric tons for 1950-55. The 181.8 million ton cumulative total underestimate of grain production during 1950-55 is then distributed over the individual years in the same proportion as the assumed underreporting of equivalent planted area during the same period.

Notes to Table 2 (Continued on facing page)

Notes to Table 2 (*Continued from facing page*)

| Production Year | Official Estimated Production (million tons) (1) | Estimated Percent Under-Reporting of Equivalent Area Planted to Grain (1955-57 Mean*=100) (2) | Percent of Estimated Under-Reporting of 181.8 Million Metric Tons (Col. 2×100 ÷44.6) (3) | Under-estimate of Grain Production (4) | Estimated Production |
|---|---|---|---|---|---|
| 1950 | 124.7 | 13.5 percent | 30.3 percent | 55.1 | 179.8 |
| 1951 | 135.1 | 11.7 percent | 26.3 percent | 47.8 | 182.9 |
| 1952 | 154.4 | 7.3 percent | 16.4 percent | 29.8 | 184.2 |
| 1953 | 156.9 | 5.7 percent | 12.7 percent | 23.1 | 180.0 |
| 1954 | 160.4 | 4.1 percent | 9.2 percent | 16.7 | 177.1 |
| 1955 | 174.8 | 2.3 percent | 5.1 percent | 9.3 | 184.1 |
| | | 44.6 percent | 100.0 percent | 181.8 | |

\* Average 121.3 million crop hectares. The mean for the three relatively normal years is used on the assumption that it may be a more accurate estimate of the real situation than the official estimate for any of the three years.

1957-60—The cumulative addition to stock in 1957-61 was 165 million metric tons (Table 1, col. 11). The 165 million tons less the 8.8 million tons purchased from abroad in 1961 and 1962 yields 156.2 million tons. This figure is regarded as representing the cumulative overestimate of net supply during 1958-60. In order to reduce the net supply by 156.2 million tons, the gross production should be reduced by 195.2 million tons if 20 per cent of the gross was wasted in processing or devoted to uses other than food. This assumed overestimate of 195.2 million is distributed as follows:

| | Production Reported (1) | The Production Reported as percent of 655 (3 year total) (2) | Million Tons (3)=(1)×(2) | Estimated Production (4)=(1)—(3) |
|---|---|---|---|---|
| 1958 | 250 | 38.2 percent | 74.6 | 175.4 |
| 1959 | 220* | 33.6 percent | 65.6 | 154.4 |
| 1960 | 185 | 28.2 percent | 55.0 | 130.0 |
| Total | 655 | | | |

\* Adjusted from an earlier claim of 270 million tons by multiplying the unrevised total of 375 million tons of 1958 by a factor of 41/70. This is the ratio of 1958 unrevised yields to 1959 yields in 4 provinces. *People's Daily*, October 15 and 20 and November 2, 1958; October 6, March 7, April 14, and June 18, 1959; *The Red Flag*, No. 18, 1959.

The underlying assumption is that the officially revised estimates or estimates based on

Notes to Table 2 (*Continued from page 87*)

official revisions still contain the same element of overstatement resulting from the discrepancy between the actual harvest and the unharvested yield.

1961—The 1961 production is estimated at not more than 10 million tons greater than that of 1960.

1962—The 1962 output is estimated at 14 percent higher than in 1961, or 160 million tons. Both the 1961 and the 1962 figures are based on Hong Kong and other Far Eastern reports.

Column (2): 20 percent of the total estimates of production is used for feed; seed waste and manufacturing.

Column (3): Same as Table 1, col. 7.

Columns (5) to (7): (a) Preliminary, based on 1960 per adult consumption.
                              (b) Preliminary, based on 1961 per adult consumption.

Column (5) is as same as column (9) in Table 1.

Reference may be made at this point to two interesting comparisons. In the first place, according to reports in late 1959 and early 1960 pertaining to substantiated grain output figures for three provinces (Kwangtung, Shantung, and Kansu), the corrected figures were from 40 to over 50 per cent smaller than the unrevised reports of 1958.[5] If the unrevised 375 million ton total were subjected to a 50 per cent discount, the result would be 187.5 million tons or the same as in 1957. This would be slightly higher than the adjusted estimate in Table 2.

In the second place, according to Jasny, the Soviet official crop estimate in 1935–39 should be subjected to a discount of 16.5 per cent in 1935, 28 per cent in 1936, 20.2 per cent in 1937, 20.0 per cent in 1938, and 22.8 per cent in 1939 if one is to arrive at barn yield.[6] According to reports in 1957,[7] methods of estimating crops in Hopei and Heilungkiang indicated that the crops were estimated in terms of biological yield. It may be presumed, therefore, that the official production estimates were virtually all based on biological yield. During 1958 and the subsequent years, labor shortage at harvest time, greater inducement to sabotage, negligence,

[5] *People's Daily*, Oct. 6, Nov. 2, and Dec. 21, 1958; Oct 7 and 20, 1959; Feb. 6, 1960.

[6] Naum Jasny, *The Socialized Agriculture of the U.S.S.R.* (Stanford, Calif.: Stanford University Press, 1949, pp. 548–744).

[7] *T'ung-chi Kung-tso* (Statistical Work), No. 19, 1957.

and theft under the commune system, and additional difficulties in harvesting large potato crops grown on hillsides may have accounted for a larger than usual discrepancy between the sown area and the harvested area and, therefore, between the biological and the barn crops. Furthermore, the apparently very large discount in 1958 was probably in part merely a compensation for inaccurate and exaggerated reports of the "biological crop" because of the field agents' inclination to report unusually high yields in the spirit of the "Great Leap Forward" in order to impress their superiors with their ideological rectitude.

## VI. A HYPOTHETICAL GROWTH TREND OF GRAIN PRODUCTION AND THE PROSPECT OF FOOD DEFICIENCY

It should be noted that the adjusted estimates for 1950–57 in Table 2 do not claim to be the actual data, which may not be available even in China. Rather, they constitute a hypothetical model that may approximate the actual conditions better than the official estimates which are notoriously inconsistent. It would, therefore, be judicious to treat the adjusted estimates essentially as an approximation with some reservation pending the availability of incontrovertibly accurate data.

On the basis of the adjusted figures for 1956–57 in Table 2, a linear trend can be fitted by least squares. The trend equation is $Yc = 180.644 + 0.373X$ ($X = 0$ in 1950 as base). Based on the projected trend values, an estimate of the deficiency between the trend value and any projected consumption requirement can then be made. Similarly, one could ascertain the gap between the trend value and actual grain production which fell considerably below the trend during the years of agricultural crisis.

As for the future, the growth of the consumption requirement would depend largely upon the rate of population increase and the obvious need to maintain a minimum level of
consumption, plus a certain degree of steady improvement.
From the point of view of increasing production above the
estimated 1963 barn crop of 160 million tons, the required
increase may be treated as the net result of a two-part effort
— (1) recovery to the trend level and (2) increase over and
above the trend value, or what is tantamount to a revision
of the trend. The latter part of the increase in production
would have to be predicated upon a new departure in farm
technology.

TABLE 3. COMPARISON BETWEEN ADJUSTED ESTIMATES OF GRAIN PRODUC-
TION AND TREND VALUE

| Production Year | Adjusted Estimate of Grain Production (1) | Estimated Trend Value (2) | Total Hypothetical Consumption Requirement of Following Year (3) | Deviation of Estimated Production From Trend* (2)—(1) | Shortfall of Trend Below Consumption Requirement (3)—(2) |
|---|---|---|---|---|---|
| 1950 | 180 | 180.6 | 172.6 | +.6 | —8.0 |
| 1951 | 183 | 181.0 | 175.9 | —2.0 | —5.1 |
| 1952 | 184 | 181.4 | 179.2 | —2.6 | —2.2 |
| 1953 | 180 | 181.8 | 181.7 | +1.8 | —.1 |
| 1954 | 177 | 182.1 | 184.3 | +5.1 | +2.2 |
| 1955 | 184 | 182.5 | 188.9 | —1.5 | +6.4 |
| 1956 | 182 | 182.9 | 194.9 | +.9 | +12.0 |
| 1957 | 185 | 183.3 | 200.0 | —1.7 | +16.7 |
| 1958 | 175 | 183.7 | 204.4 | +8.7 | +20.7 |
| 1959 | 154 | 184.0 | 208.7 | +30.0 | +24.7 |
| 1960 | 130 | 184.4 | 212.1 | +54.4 | +27.7 |
| 1961 | 140 | 184.8 | 214.8 | +44.8 | +30.0 |
| 1962 | 160 | 185.2 | 217.6 | +25.2 | +32.4 |
| 1963 | 183† | 185.6 | 220.0 | +2.6 | +34.4 |

*(+) indicates actual production falling short of trend value
† Preliminary
    Col. 1: Table 2
    Col. 2: Computed from equation
    Col. 3: 1950-55, Cols. (1)—[(6)+(3)] in Table 2
1956-63, estimated at 245 kg. of processed grain per adult and 20 per cent of gross output
for other uses than direct consumption as food for midyear population as in note 9, Table 1.

## VII.  PRODUCTIVITY AND INSTITUTIONAL CHANGE

Returning to the contention that institutional change would increase labor productivity and therefore output per man *as well as* per unit area, one may now inquire whether actual experience has borne out this hypothesis. The redistributed land and the small owner cultivators created during the land reform period constituted such a brief and transitory stage that there was no basis for a real comparison with the previous record. Available estimates of yield per hectare in 1955, when a considerable number of cooperative farms were already in existence, however, showed that the results were generally unfavorable in comparison with the average yields of 1931–37 for China proper, with the exception of paddy rice, and that it was uniformally unfavorable in comparison with the most frequent yields in 1929–33.

In terms of the farmer's income, Liao Lu-yen, Communist China's Minister of Agriculture, stated in early 1958 that about 30 per cent of the agricultural cooperatives in China (46 per cent of the cooperatives in some provinces) had by then *caught up* with local "well-to-do middle peasants" in their production level, and that 20 per cent of the cooperatives in China had caught up with the local "well-to-do middle peasants" in income standard.[8] It should be noted in passing that the "middle peasants" were in pre-Communist China the small farmers whose farms were too small to be efficient. As a whole, according to Liao, 20–30 per cent of the cooperatives in China had by early 1958 (before the establishment of the communes) reached the level of the "well-to-do middle peasants." Furthermore, a November 1957 study stated that surveys of agricultural cooperatives of different types in various places showed that the grain

[8] *Hsüeh-hsi* (Study) (Peking), No. 3, Feb. 1958.

output per unit area of the "well-to-do middle peasants" was generally about 20 per cent higher than that of the newly established cooperatives, and that the former's per capita income was about 30 per cent higher than the corresponding figure in the cooperatives.[9]

TABLE 4. COMPARATIVE DATA ON CROP YIELDS
(KILOGRAMS PER HECTARE)

|  | 1952 Communist China | 1955 Communist China | 1931-37 Average China Proper | 1929-33 Most Frequent Yields Mainland China |
|---|---|---|---|---|
| Paddy | 2,445 | 2,674 | 2,532 | 2,972-(2,775)*** |
| Wheat | 735 | 858 | 1,078 | 1,077-1,213 |
| Corn | 1,343 ⎫ | | 1,379 | 1,321 |
| Kaoliang | 1,178 ⎬ | 1,047* | 1,366 | 1,279 |
| Millet | 1,140 ⎭ | | 1,178† | 1,178† |
| Tubers (original weight) | 7,500** | 7,516** | 7,900 | 5,837 |

* Miscellaneous grains
** Mostly sweet potatoes
† Weighted average of millet and proso millet
*** The figure of 2,972 is a mean for *all* types of rice per crop hectare. The figure of 2,775 is the median for 22 provinces. See Buck, p. 17, this monograph. In *Land Utilization, loc. cit.*, the yield for the main crop of rice and glutinous rice is 3,273-3,384.
Sources: 1952, *K'o-hsüeh T'ung-pao* (Science Bulletin), No. 5, 1954.
1955, computed from *Jen-min Shou-ts'e* (People's Handbook), 1957, pp. 470-471.
1931-37, T. H. Shen, *op. cit.*, 1951.
1929-33, John Lossing Buck, *Land Utilization in China*, 1937, pp. 224-225 except for paddy.

Inasmuch as statistics of yield and income under the commune became exceedingly unreliable, and inasmuch as the sharp decline in agricultural, and particularly grain, output began in 1959, any comparison of yield and labor productivity based on these statistics with corresponding data under the cooperative system would be misleading. However, because of the undeniable agricultural crisis, one would assume that the communes definitely failed to evoke any real in-

[9] *Cheng-chi Hsüeh-hsi* (Political Study), No. 11, Nov. 1957.

crease in output, even though there may have been a large rise of labor input during the early phase of the commune movement in 1958-59. The prodigious expenditure of labor in irrigation, deep plowing, and the application of fertilizers is well known and may be obtained from a number of sample studies.[10]

Apparently, the cooperative farm did not succeed in raising unit area yield. On the other hand, from the point of view of the Communist authorities, it did offer two advantages over the individual farm. First, the formation of the cooperative farm thwarted any tendency for the emergence of a new "rich peasant" class which probably would have occured had the owner-cultivators created under the land reform been left to their own devices. Ideologically and politically this was a significant advantage from the point of view of the Communist party. In the second place, on the basis of an income study undertaken in 1957 that covered 228 agricultural cooperatives in 24 provinces, it was found that communal accumulation (including possibly proceeds from the government's compulsory purchases applied to reduce existing indebtedness to the government), together with addition to share capital in the cooperative, and work performed on construction projects without pay constituted some 15 per cent of income (i.e., the sum of the same items and personal income distributed to the commune members). This relatively high, though perhaps still inadequate, rural saving-income ratio in the cooperative was probably one of the reasons why the Communist authorities decided to accelerate the completion of the cooperative farm movement in 1956, although it had originally been scheduled for 1958, and to maintain an even higher ratio. At the same time, according to the same survey, the per capita personal income was probably around 48 to 56 yuan a year. This may be

[10] See, for instance, the report on the Hung-kuang people's commune in the *People's Daily*, April 18, 1959.

compared with a per capita rural income of 58 yuan in
1931–36 at prewar prices.[11] Thus, one may assume that the
accelerated transition to the cooperative arm was due to the
desire to increase the rate of saving in the agricultural sector,
while the failure of production to rise in spite of the larger
operating units (compared with the individual farm) was a
result of inexperience, poorly directed production planning,
and adverse effects of the cooperative form of organization
on incentive.

The formation of the cooperative farm meant that persons
who had hitherto been underemployed but had been supported by other members of their households could no longer
be so supported in the cooperatives because of the latter's
need for stricter cost accounting. In the circumstances, there
was some large-scale population movement from the villages
to the cities. Accordingly, increased pressure was felt by the
Communist authorities to accelerate the creation of alternative forms of employment. It is quite possible that this consideration may have contributed to the subsequent decision
to develop rural industry in the commune as a part of the
small industry movement.

The commune, in its turn, was significant as a form of
organization of the labor force. It increased labor mobility
and expanded the size of the labor force which could now be
engaged in agricultural as well as nonagricultural activities
on an around-the-clock-full-employment basis. However, as
mentioned earlier, the operating unit of farming in the
commune was the "production brigade," which corresponded
roughly to the cooperative farm in size. Thus, the economic
justification of the commune did not lie in any expected increase in farm size, but rather in the expansion of labor
intensive, nonagricultural projects and the much higher
saving-income ratio which the commune made possible.

[11] Yuan-li Wu, *op. cit.*, 1961, p. 25.

In practice, however, because of poor cost accounting practice in the commune, the employment of nonpaid labor, and the high mobility of labor, many of the industrial and agricultural projects begun in the commune were not completed. Labor was shifted from one type of work to another without the administrators' realization that such shifts, though entailing no monetary expenditure, did incur "opportunity costs" that consisted of the unfinished work elsewhere. Deep-plowing, irrigation work, collection and application of manure, collection and transportation of ore for the "backyard iron furnaces," and many other demanding tasks were all extremely costly in terms of labor input. At the same time, direction of farm work by centralized directives proved to be not only ineffective but actually damaging. While poor weather conditions may have played their part in the reduction of agricultural output in 1959 and the later years, mismanagement under the commune and an incentive crisis attributable equally to the communal form of organization and the high saving-income ratio were the true culprits. This explains why the major effort—which began in 1961 and was redoubled in 1962—to revitalize agriculture has essentially consisted of some radical modifications of the commune system.

## VIII. REORGANIZATION OF THE COMMUNE AND THE PRODUCTION AND DISTRIBUTION SYSTEM

As a result of subdivision, the number of communes increased from 24,000 to nearly 100,000 in 1962 while the number of production brigades rose to 500,000.[12] This decrease in the size of the commune is symptomatic of some very radical and farreaching changes which took place during 1961–62.

[12] *New China Yearbook* (Tokyo), July 1962, pp. 19–20.

First, in May 1961, a new set of regulations governing the organization of the commune was promulgated by the Communist authorities. These regulations were introduced to bring some degree of uniformity to the diverse developments which had occured in communes in different parts of the country since the winter of 1960. In the last quarter of 1961, both the commune and the production brigade were further downgraded. Finally, in September 1962, the decision was handed down from the Communist party of China to continue its new policy of emphasizing the "production team" while calling at the same time for the consolidation of the spirit of collectivization in the agricultural sector.

In order to understand the significance of these changes, the mid-1961 regulations with respect to ownership of property, control over the use of the means of production, decision-making in implementation, and the principles and methods employed in distributing output should be studied. In summary, these regulations provided for the concentration of decision-making on production in the hands of the peasants below the commune level, the curtailment of the powers of the commune which had led to the abuse of labor mobility and frequent changes in production plans, restoration of some private production for their own account by the peasants, the determination of the peasants' compensation more closely in line with the amount of work performed, and an increase in the ratios of consumption to income and of monetary compensation to ratios in kind. However, as the *People's Daily* stated on August 29, 1961, as of that time, the production brigade still remained as the independent accounting unit in contrast to the smaller production team which had again assumed its precollectivization role as the basic unit in organizing production.

A further step was taken in January 1962 when the official press took the line that agricultural recovery depended upon the "productive activism" of the masses, and that this could be accomplished only through the Communist party's policy to employ the production team as the accounting unit.[13] The same paper then spoke of the over-expansion of the production brigade which had led to "egalitarianism" in distributing output to the detriment of incentive. Apparently, since this further revision of policy, distribution becomes vested in the hands of the production team: the team now owns both the land and the greater part of the equipment and draught animals it uses. These changes are said to be desirable because, until mechanization can become the rule, the smaller production and distribution units would be more adapted to the present stage of development of Chinese agriculture. Thus, the reversal of policy really represents an effort to return to a production unit corresponding more closely to the larger farm of the pre-Communist period, while attempts are made to preserve the necessary ideological framework and government control required. With the exception of a small number of areas, the production team became the basic accounting as well as production unit in 1963.

Unfortunately for the Communist planners, a dilemma between incentive and government control remains. As the *Southern Daily* of Canton stated on April 6, 1963, "Some well-to-do middle peasants have said, 'The government needs only to control the collection and purchasing of grain; it should not bother about how agricultural production is done.' . . . The new and old upper middle peasants have a comparatively strong spontaneous tendency toward capitalism. . . ." If such a spontaneous tendency is to be combated, would the need for ideological control interfere with the provision of adequate incentives and the restoration of production?

[13] *People's Daily*, January 1, 1962.

## IX.  TECHNOLOGICAL IMPROVEMENTS
## IN AGRICULTURE

During the 1958–59 commune movement and the concomitant drive to increase crop production, emphasis was placed on the more intensive application of labor input in the form of more irrigation works, more deep-plowing, more application of natural fertilizer and compost, closer planting, and continuous field supervision. While some of these measures were efforts to improve the methods of cultivation, they rested on the traditional technological base. In contrast, the effort to bring about agricultural recovery since 1961 has been concentrated on more radical technological improvements, particularly in the electrification of irrigation facilities, a greater degree of mechanization, and more intensive use of chemical fertilizers.

One estimate puts the size of irrigated land in 1962–63 at about 50 million hectares.[14] Of these, the total area that could be irrigated by electrically operated pumping facilities in 1962 would probably amount to 4.8 million hectares as compared with 3.3 million hectares at the end of 1961.[15] The 1962 estimate is based on a utilization rate of 3.2 hectares per kilowatt of pumping facility and 1.5 million kilowatt of electrical pumping equipment. In 1963, the area of irrigated land possessing electrically operated pumping facilities was probably around 6.4 million hectares.[16]

A so-called mechanization program in agriculture has thus far consisted of an increase in the number of tractors available. In terms of 15 horse-power standard units, the number

---

[14] *Kung-jen Jih-pao* (The Worker's Daily [Peking]), March 8, 1961, reported an increase in irrigated area of 20 million hectares in 1958–60, which, when added to a total of 34.7 million hectares in 1957, gives us a new total of 54.7 million hectares.

[15] *People's Daily*, Oct. 23, 1961.

[16] NCNA, April 12, 1963.

increased from 59,000 units in 1959 to 81,000 in 1960, to 90,000 in 1961, and to approximately 100,000 at the end of 1962.[17] Since, according to Chinese reports, a standard tractor can on the average probably cultivate only 100 hectares of land, the increment in hectares that can be machine cultivated during the 1961–62 period was extremely small. Some of the large state farms, where the degree of mechanization is higher, have reported an increase in labor productivity as high as 70 per cent when comparison is made between "semi-mechanization" and the employment of traditional farm implements, and another 150 per cent more if the comparison is between "semi-mechanization" and "mechanization." [18] On the other hand, by far the most important role of the machine manufacturing enterprises, many of which have been assigned to the specific task of aiding agriculture, has been the production of simple farm implements although some of these may be of improved design. The same enterprises have been kept busy in repair work. Reports from different parts of the country often complain of unskilled handling of machinery and indifferent maintenance and high replacement requirements, both complicated by the existence of machines of many different makes.

Finally, domestic production of chemical fertilizers in 1958 was below a million tons while import at the same time was about 1.5 million tons. Production in 1962 was approximately 2 million tons while output in 1963 was probably 2.6 million tons. Imports during the same period were 1.2 million tons in 1962 and 1.7 million tons in 1963.

These tentative and sketchy statistics would seem to show that the ascertainable quantitative effect of the "technological revolution" on the 1962 and 1963 harvests was not particularly significant. Hence, the 10 to 15 per cent increase in

[17] *Far Eastern Economic Review* (Hong Kong), Vol. XXXIX, No. 7 (Feb. 14, 1963), pp. 309–310; and *China Weekly* (Hong Kong), No. 515 (Nov. 1962), pp. 175–182.
[18] *Economic Research* (Peking), No. 3 (March 1963), p. 5.

grain output during 1961–62 and the probably greater increase in 1962–63, both of which fell well below the trend values, could not be attributed to the beneficial effects of the technological improvements. On the other hand, any large increase above the trend values in the future would have to be predicated upon technological improvements. On the basis of projected population increments, it should thus not be too difficult for Communist China's planners to forecast the demand for investment in chemical fertilizers, fertilizer plants, other farm chemicals, and electric and other equipment necessary for the continued expansion of mechanization and electrification. What this would mean in terms of foreign exchange requirement and the country's residual import capacity for other purposes can then be derived.

It is entirely conceivable that because of the needs of the agricultural sector, the availability of exchange may become the effective constraint to the import of industrial equipment and raw materials other than those destined for the agricultural sector. Consequently, success in agricultural recovery may become a prerequisite of economic growth in general. The alternative of importing food would be even more expensive unless large non-agricultural exports can be developed. Such a development, however, cannot be expected to take place without further industrial expansion, which is precluded by assumption in the absence of greater growth in agriculture.

OWEN L. DAWSON

# Fertilizer Supply and Food Requirements

## I. INTRODUCTION

Since agriculture is still the basis of the Chinese economy, much of mainland China's future economic progress will depend upon the ability of the agricultural sector to produce enough for consumption and trade. In this respect, the record shows that (1) agricultural production was able to score only a moderate advance from the time of the Communist takeover in 1949 up to 1958, and (2) by dint of stringent and compulsory economics on the part of the farmers, agricultural exports were maintained at a high enough level to provide for the greater part of the country's foreign exchange requirements. However, food grain production per capita remained at close to the minimum level, and, since 1958, has even fallen well below it. The problem of expanding production to meet the needs of the spiraling population has become increasingly urgent, especially after the recent poor crop years and the breakdown of an overorganized system of agricultural controls. Both in China and in the outside world there is probably agreement on one point: namely, that the Communist authorities gave agriculture far too little attention and expected far too much from it.

Because of the pressure exerted over many centuries by a dense and growing population on the limited land resources of China, yields of food crops have tended toward a static level despite the use of all available organic fertilizer. The sustained higher yields needed to support a growing population, as has become increasingly clear, can be attained only through extensive use of chemical fertilizer. Yet, mainland China at present is near the bottom of the list of important countries in the use of chemical fertilizer per hectare of cultivated land; hence, the colossal problem of setting up an adequate fertilizer industry must be faced.

Although organic fertilizer has been used for centuries in China, its effect in increasing yields has not been adequately calculated to permit derivation of an estimate of the need for supplemental chemical fertilizer. Nor is the state of statistical information on the economic use of chemical fertilizer in China at all satisfactory. While estimates of the long-run requirements for chemical fertilizer in Japan, Taiwan, and India are available, only very rough estimates, based on prewar experimental data, have been made for mainland China. Since the development of a large chemical fertilizer industry would require enormous investment in machinery (including imported equipment) and trained manpower, the importance of a sound estimate of Communist China's fertilizer needs in her future economic development cannot be overemphasized.

The purpose of this paper is to fill part of this gap in information by focusing attention on the potential of food grain production in China, the implied demand for fertilizer, and the impact of China's efforts to meet these deficits on the world's markets.

Several preliminary points may be profitably clarified at this juncture. First, estimates on chemical fertilizer are given in this report both in terms of the principal ingredients—i.e., N, $P_2O_5$, and $K_2O$—and in gross quantities. This is in conformity with prewar and current practice in China, as well as in Taiwan and Japan, where total gross tonnage is used. At the same time, it is recognized that the present tendency is to use chemical fertilizer in more concentrated forms. The present ratio of gross fertilizer materials to total crop nutrients (N, $P_2O_5$ and $K_2O$) in Taiwan and Japan is about 4.4 to 1, whereas formerly it was about 5 to 1; even greater concentration will probably prevail in another ten years. Because of these trends in practice, we shall attempt to estimate mainland China's requirements in 1972 in terms of both gross quantity of fertilizer and soil nutritive elements.

Second, special attention is called to the use of food grains in the calculation of food requirements. As a measure of caloric requirements, it has become an increasingly accepted practice in many countries to allow some 15 per cent of the total caloric requirements for other foods. It is true that a portion of the diet should be composed of proteins, fats, minerals, and vitamins and that these elements greatly affect health and stamina, but, this topic must be left to discussion on some other occasion.

Third, wherever possible, Chinese sources on organic fertilizer have been used, and generous allowance has been made for the effect of other factors in increasing the yield potential. Consequently, the final estimate of chemical fertilizer requirement in this paper is probably conservative; different approaches by other analysts could suggest higher requirements.

## II. SOME BACKGROUND INFORMATION ON FOOD AND POPULATION

A moderate upward trend in Communist China's agricultural production was achieved during her First Five Year Plan (1953–57). This was accomplished primarily by continuing past improvements—though with increased emphasis —in various agricultural techniques, including land reclamation and the more efficient use of water resources. In addition, Communist policy also strove to bring about a large increase in the supply of organic fertilizer while trying to produce chemical fertilizer in local plants.

Such measures, however, proved inadequate in the long run. For, after more than a decade of Communist efforts to increase agricultural production, the Chinese mainland, far from enjoying abundance, has experienced a severe food shortage. Some 5.5 to 6 million tons of grain had to be imported annually during 1961 and 1962 in order to make up the deficiency, similar imports are still continuing. The Communist admit serious harvest failures, although they prefer to point to three years of bad weather for an explanation. Regardless of the causes, there is incontrovertible evidence of widespread malnutrition. While the crop in 1962 was better than in the previous two years, it was still more than 20 million metric tons below the minimum adequate consumption requirement, even on the basis of a rather optimistic estimate of 190 million metric tons of gross grain crop produced and a total requirement of some 215 million metric tons for a population of around 713 million at the close of 1962.

Some of the blame may be attributed to Communist organizational and technical mistakes during the years of the widely publicized "Great Leap Forward" and to the accompanying commune system that made the "Leap" possible. Communist-style incentives and organization have obviously fallen far short of attaining the vast increases in production predicted and promised. But an even more fundamental problem is the possibility that the country's food grain production might prove insufficient even in the absence of these errors.

Behind this unhappy picture is the specter of China's reportedly mushrooming population. While estimates of the population of mainland China vary rather widely, it appears probable that more than 720 million people live in mainland China at present. At a net annual growth rate of two per cent, which would represent a slight decline from that of the 1950's, the population of China should pass 880 million by 1972.[1]

An official policy to restrain consumption, reinforced by the moderate increase in output and the expanding population, conspired to keep the per capita food supply under the Communists, even in the best years, barely at the prewar level of 1931–37 when there was, on the whole, an adequate quantity of food grains. The quality of the diet was poor, distribution was uneven, and in bad years, famine stalked large areas. Through a better collection and distribution system, the new regime was able to even out to some extent the use of available supplies, but there were still highly favored groups. Furthermore, the rigid grain collection program was maintained even in the recent bad years, which resulted in reduction of the local emergency stocks that were traditionally maintained, so that remote or less important economic groups suffered even more than usual during a period of food shortage.

The manner in which available grain supply per head has changed may be appreciated at this point if we bear in mind a few salient facts. In the first place, by 1952, on the eve of the First Five Year Plan, food grain crops production is believed to have recovered to the prewar (1931–37) average of about 170 million metric tons. Over the same years, however, the population may have increased about 10 per cent. The grossly inflated claims in 1958 first put food grain production at 350 million metric tons. Although the claim was later scaled down to 250 million metric tons by the Communists themselves, it was still far out of line with available evidence. It should also be noted parenthetically that the weather during 1958 was, on the whole, better than usual. In the three years after 1958, gross production is believed to have fallen well below 200 million metric tons per annum.

[1] U.S. Census Bureau, series of estimates furnished the author.

In view of the increasing population, per capita grain availability fell to much below the prewar level. As mentioned earlier, large-scale imports were required to remedy the deficit in part. No doubt these imports were used to support the rations of favored groups while the masses were inadequately fed.

## Communist China's Efforts to Date to Increase Fertilizer Supplies

Communist China has made strenuous efforts to make fuller use of the country's available organic fertilizer supply. But even maximum use in this respect would still be insufficient in view of the amount of fertilizer needed to increase yields. The consequent need for a huge expansion of chemical fertilizer production is recognized by high Communist Chinese officials. Thus, Liao Lu-yen, Communist Minister of Agriculture, stated in 1956 that the Twelve-Year Plan (1956–67) for agricultural development envisaged an annual requirement of 20 million metric tons gross of nitrogenous fertilizer (such as ammonium sulphate). With appropriate supplements of phosphorus and potassium, this would mean some 33 million metric tons of gross chemical fertilizer. Production of nitrogenous fertilizer in 1956, on the other hand, was about 663,000 metric tons, augmented by 837,000 tons of imports. For 1958, the reported figures were: production, 1,244,000 tons; imports, 1,464,000 tons. Production in 1963 was estimated at about 2.6 million metric tons while imports were 1.5 million metric tons.[2]

## Comparison with Taiwan and Japan

The importance of chemical fertilizer to Communist China can be better appreciated if her use of organic and

[2] *Central Directorate of Statistics,* Communist China, Peking; Ministries of Agriculture and Forestry, Nationalist China, Taipei; and Government of Japan.

chemical fertilizers in food production and the corresponding usage in Taiwan and Japan are compared. Taiwan and
Japan have used organic fertilizer extensively for a number
of decades. Yet both countries have found it necessary to
have recourse to very large supplements of chemical fertilizer
in order to increase crop yields. Furthermore, there are many
similarities as to the conditions of crop cultivation in all
three areas. The people of Taiwan are predominantly of
Chinese stock descended from mainland farmers. The Japanese during their rule of some 50 years continually introduced improved agricultural methods into Taiwan. These
innovations have been followed up and improved upon by
Nationalist Chinese agricultural specialists during the past
fifteen years. There is, therefore, an interlocking relationship
between Taiwan and Japan that makes the comparison with
Communist China particularly significant.

Natural conditions of irrigation, available water resources,
and the volume and distribution of rainfall in Taiwan and
Japan are such that it has been possible to increase the proportion of rice and other high-yield crops through the use
of chemical fertilizer. If her water resources were fully uti-
lized, it might be possible to achieve comparable increase on
40 to 50 per cent of the cultivated area in mainland China.
Experimental test plots on the mainland have indicated a
great potential increase not only in the rice yield but also
of other food grains when they are grown on land suitable
for the use of chemical fertilizer.

Some of the basic data for an initial comparison of the
three areas are presented in Table 1. (Data for further comparisons are given in Tables 2 and 3 in the next section.)

*A Method of Estimating Future Chemical Fertilizer Needs*

The need for chemical fertilizer in Communist China is
generally recognized. We shall now attempt to estimate Communist China's minimum chemical fertilizer requirements

TABLE 1. COMPARATIVE DATA ON POPULATION, ANIMAL UNITS, LAND AREA, AND FOOD GRAIN CROP PRODUCTION IN COMMUNIST CHINA, TAIWAN AND JAPAN, 1956[1]

| | COUNTRIES | | | RATIO TO CHINA | | |
|---|---|---|---|---|---|---|
| | China | Taiwan | Japan | China | Taiwan | Japan |
| Cult. land (million hectares)[2] | 112.0 | 0.875 | 6.01 | 100 | .8 | 5.0 |
| Crop area (million hectares)[3] | 159.0 | 1,712.0 | 8.30 | 100 | 1.07 | 5.22 |
| Double crop index[4] | 142.0 | 195.0 | 138.0 | 100 | 137.0 | 97.0 |
| Million hectares of food grain crops | 124.0 | 1.054 | 6.103 | 100 | 0.85 | 4.92 |
| Ratio of food grain to total crop area[5] | 78.0 | 63.0 | 78.0 | 100 | 81.0 | 100.0 |
| Animal units (million)[6] | 116.0 | 1.3 | 5.0 | 100 | 1.11 | 4.31 |
| Ratio of animal units to cult. land[7] | 103.5 | 149.0 | 88.0 | 100 | 144.0 | 85.0 |
| Population (million) | 625.0 | 9.8 | 90.0 | 100 | 1.55 | 14.4 |
| Ratio of population to cult. area[8] | 5.6 | 12.0 | 15.8 | 100 | 214.0 | 282.0 |
| Food crops (million tons) of cereals and potatoes[9] | 182.5 | 3,063.0 | 20.62 | 100 | 1.7 | 11.3 |
| Kg/per food grain crop hectare[10] | 1,471.0 | 2,906.0 | 3,369.0 | 100 | 197.0 | 229.0 |
| Population/animal units[11] | 5.4 | 7.5 | 18.0 | 100 | 139.0 | 333.0 |

[1] Based on official sources—Central Directorate of Statistics, Communist China, Ministers of Agricultural and Forestry, Taiwan and Tokyo. The table is designed to show the position of the three areas with respect to basic factors of potential grain production. Organic fertilizer is to a large extent a function of population, animal units, and crop residues. Total food grain crop production depends on the intensity of land use for food crops which is determined by climate, water, and soil conditions, and application of fertilizer, together with progressive agricultural techniques.

[2] All land used for agricultural purposes.

[3] Crop area includes all area planted to agricultural crops produced by either single or multiple cropping.

[4] Ratio of crop area to cultivated land. It shows the intensity of food crop production on available land. The potentiality depends on water, climate, growing season, soil fertility, and other factors, including good crop management, of rotations and variety adaptation.

[5] Shows relation of food grain crops to all crops.

[6] The animal units are computed on the basis of 1 cow or horse as equivalent to 5 hogs, 7 sheep or goats, or 100 chickens.

[7] Shows number of livestock in relation to cultivated land, which would affect the availability of organic fertilizer.

[8] This ratio shows the pressure of population on crop land and serves as an indication of the need to increase yields. While the index could be increased considerably in mainland China the potential level is much less than in Taiwan and Japan.

[9] Potatoes are converted to equivalent weights of cereals at the rate of 4 to 1.

[10] The yield per food grain crop hectare in Taiwan is lower than that of Japan, but more is produced per unit of cultivated land owing to the much higher multiple crop index (4) which has risen further since 1956.

[11] If the ratio of population to livestock animal units increases to 6, a population of 882 million in 1972 would indicate the number of animal units at 147 million. If it increased to 65, the number of animal units would be 140 million.

for the period through 1972. The principal assumptions and related considerations in this estimate are as follows:

1. Minimum food grain needs are estimated on the basis of assumed population growth rates and minimum nutritional requirements, which are checked against known prewar per capita consumption levels.

2. Allowance is made for possible increases in production attributable to expansion of crop area and improved techniques.

3. Chemical fertilizer requirements are calculated by taking into account the availability of organic fertilizer, the input of crop nutrients and their removal from the soil, and increase in the use of chemical fertilizer and its effect in the light of similar experience in pre-Communist China, Japan, and Taiwan. The probable increase in fertilizer production is estimated in the same light.

4. Finally, estimates are made of the possible short fall in the supply of chemical fertilizer and the consequent effects on the economy.

## III. EFFECT OF CHEMICAL FERTILIZER APPLICATION IN MAINLAND CHINA, TAIWAN, AND JAPAN

### Mainland China

Beginning in 1935, experiments carried out by N. F. Chang and H. L. Richardson in 170 field experiments at widely scattered locations in 14 provinces in mainland China showed that 83 per cent of the soils tested gave significant response to one or more nutrients. Nitrogen deficiency was evident in 74 per cent of the soils, phosphate in 38 per cent, and potash in only 12 per cent.[3] From these findings the authors concluded that, if chemical fertilizers were used only on

[3] N. F. Chang and H. L. Richardson, "Use of Soil Fertilizers in China," *Nature*, Vol. XLIX, No. 3780 (April 11, 1942).

soils giving significant responses in experiments at an application rate of 54 pounds per acre, it would be possible to increase the total production of crops in mainland China by one-third to one-half. (The proportions of the three elements —N, $P_2O_5$, and $K_2O$—were not clearly defined.) In this connection, it is important to mention Dr. T. H. Shen's emphasis on supplementing local manures by chemical fertilizer.[4] According to Shen, where water is not a limiting factor, crop production could be increased by about 25 per cent; his minimum estimate of chemical fertilizer requirement is 15 million metric tons.

Dr. Richardson, in a more complete statement of his work in prewar China [5] involving 300 identical experiments in areas considered fairly representative of the rice-growing region, declares that treatment with 60 kilograms of N, $P_2O_5$, and $K_2O$ per hectare increased the yield of paddy rice by 847 kilograms over the yield obtainable without fertilizer, i.e., 2,385 kilograms per hectare—an average response of 36 per cent. If the rate of application were raised to the level actually used by the farmers of Taiwan and Japan, the yield could be raised to a much higher level. Data from the experiment response curves indicate that, if N were applied at such a rate (90 kilograms per hectare) in addition to phosphate and potash applied to the standard rates and with the usual local manures, the per hectare yield could be increased by 46 per cent. This would raise the yield of paddy rice to some 3,863 kilograms per hectare.

Richardson's appraisal of potentials is even more optimistic in the following statement:

"Modest estimates based on experiments in China and Japan indicate that, along with the additional fertilizer, improved

[4] T. H. Shen, *Agricultural Resources of China* (Ithaca, N. Y.: Cornell University Press, 1951).

[5] H. L. Richardson, *Increasing World Food Supplies through Greater Food Production* (London: Imperial Chemical Industries). Reprinted from *Outlook on Agriculture,* Vol. III (Nov. 1, 1960), p. 10.

varieties could add 15 per cent; better cultural methods and water control, 15 per cent; and pest and disease control, 10 per cent; giving a total of 40 per cent, or a combined increase attributable to all improvements of 86 per cent in the rice region raising the yield of paddy rice per hectare to 4,886 kg. which is almost the same as that achieved by Japan."

If the effort were confined to districts favorable in soil and climate, he believes it could still further be increased.

Less data are available from these tests regarding summer dry land cereals such as millets, sorghum, and maize. A response of some 42 per cent was indicated in a smaller number of experiments (*ibid.,* p. 11).

If we agree that such increases in yield are within the realm of possibility under the assumption of an optimum supply of chemical fertilizer and employment of all the improved techniques, it would still take a considerable number of years to raise average yields to the indicated levels. The experiences of Taiwan and Japan are illustrative of the time and effort needed.

## Taiwan

By 1958, the yield of rice in Taiwan was almost 75 per cent greater than at the beginning of the century. Although, at 3,194 kilograms per hectare it was still well below Japan's yield per rice hectare (4,620 kilograms), the large proportion of double cropping in Taiwan resulted in an average annual output per crop area that was the largest in the Orient. For 1962, the paddy rice yield in Taiwan was placed at 3,486 kilograms per hectare.

As of April 1956, experiments showed that the optimum rate was 60–80 kilograms per hectare of N (equivalent to 300–400 of $[NH_4]_2SO_4$). For each kilogram this gives 2.16–2.72 kilograms of paddy for the first crop, or 1.40–1.76 kilograms for the second crop. The optimum rate of $P_2O_5$ was

40 kilograms per hectare or 220 kilograms per hectare of calcium superphosphate, which would raise the yield by 0.47 paddy rice per hectare per kilogram, and by 0.51 for the second crop. For $K_2O$, an application of 40 kilograms (or 80 kilograms for KCL) gave an increment of 1.05 kg per hectare per kilograms for the first crop and 1.35 for the second crop.[6] Furthermore, the increment of rice yield could be profitably maintained by application of N up to 120 kilograms per hectare. If we take 120 kg/hec. as a standard rate, the yield of paddy rice could be increased at 8.7 to 10.2 kilograms per kilogram of N for the first crop and 6.1–7.1 kilograms for the second crop. The respective percentages of increased production would be 37–57 per cent and 29–34 per cent. These results were obtained from experiments in 117 localities in 1929–1942, and in 36 localities in 1953.[7]

Taiwan's fertilizer requirements for 1970 were worked out in August 1958, at the then current rate of development, to be 100,000–110,000 metric tons of N, 40,000–43,000 tons of $P_2O_5$, and 33,000–38,000 tons of $K_2O$. At an accelerated rate of development, the requirements were estimated at N, 130,000 metric tons; $P_2O_5$, 50,000 metric tons; and $K_2O$, 49,000 metric tons. Acceleration of development would depend upon the existence of favorable prices and other factors. At the current rate of development in the use of chemical fertilizer, the tonnage of the three elements required for the 920,000 hectares of rice planned for 1970 was calculated at N, 92,000; $P_2O_5$, 36,800; $K_2O$, 27,600, or an aggregate of 710,000 metric tons.[8] If other crops were in-

[6] H. F. Chu (Senior Specialist, Plant Industry Division, Joint Commission on Rural Reconstruction), *Has the Application of Chemical Fertilizer in Taiwan Reached a Maximum?* P.I.D. Doc. C-004, pp. 3–4, Taipei, April 1956.

[7] *Fertilizer Response Curves for Paddy in Taiwan,* FAO Rice Working Party on Fertilizer, International Rice Commission, Fourth Meeting, Tokyo, Oct. 4–10, 1954, p. 4.

[8] *Estimation of the Fertilizer Requirement in 1970,* J.C.R.R., P.I.D. Doc C-048, Taipei, Aug. 11, 1958.

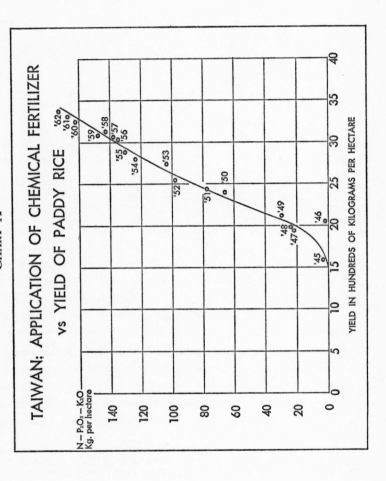

CHART A

TAIWAN: APPLICATION OF CHEMICAL FERTILIZER
vs YIELD OF PADDY RICE

N – P₂O₅ – K₂O
Kg. per hectare

YIELD IN HUNDREDS OF KILOGRAMS PER HECTARE

cluded, the requirement would be 1,034,510 tons (*ibid.*).

If chemical fertilizer were applied at an equivalent rate in mainland areas where food grain and other crops could use it profitably, some 50 to 60 million metric tons of gross chemical fertilizer would be required. This would seem to indicate a great potential demand if the fertilizer can be manufactured, distributed, and applied in accordance with regional test results.

The dramatic effect of chemical fertilizer application on paddy rice production in Taiwan can be seen from the historical data on fertilizer use and yield response in the peak prewar year of 1938 and again in 1945–61. The general crop conditions in 1938 were favorable, and 105.2 kilograms per hectare of the chief chemical fertilizer nutrients (N, $P_2O_5$, and $K_2O$) were used. The result was a phenomenal yield of 2,942 kilograms per hectare of paddy rice. Due to war conditions, almost no chemical fertilizer was used in 1945–46, and the yield dropped to 1,661 kilograms per hectare. However, from then on, the quantity used advanced steadily to 143.5 kilograms in 1958 and 167 kilograms in 1961, while the yields to 3,189 and 3,376 kilograms per hectare respectively. Thus, as shown in Chart A, an increase in use of some 143 kilograms of fertilizer nutrients from 1945 to 1958 was associated with an 1,528-kilogram advance in the yield of paddy rice. The 169-kilogram increase in use up to 1961 was associated with a further yield increase of 1,715 kilograms per hectare. The increase is still continuing and is obviously bringing about important economic benefits.[9] It must be recognized, of course, that improvements in agricultural techniques and fuller use of organic fertilizer,[10] especially through the compost program, have also played their part.

[9] *Economic Appraisal of Fertilizer Application on Rice,* J.C.R.R., P.I.D. Doc C-023, Taipei, Aug. 31, 1957.

[10] See Appendix Table 2 for fertilizer nutrients from organic and chemical sources.

## Japan

The experience of Japan's thorough going program of fertilizer use for more than half a century is an example of what is possible whenever soil needs are determined scientifically and appropriate techniques are employed to achieve the most efficient results in crop yields.

Japan's record of increase in yield of paddy rice, with chemical fertilizer amounting to 80 per cent of the total fertilizers used, has been most spectacular. In the 1890's, it was about the same level as the present yield in mainland China, i.e., around 2,500 kilograms per hectare; it now exceeds 4,500 kilograms per hectare. A mean increase of some 28.5 kilograms per hectare for each year was achieved in the 70-year period. The intensive use of chemical fertilizer has been accompanied by improved techniques of crop development under conditions promoting the maximum efficiency of the fertilizer.[11]

In 1962, Japan used some seven million tons of chemical fertilizer on about eight million crop hectares. If the same rate were applied to the 40 per cent of crop hectares in China where fertilizer probably can be used effectively, given the lack of water in many areas, total consumption would reach 60 million metric tons.

Japan's accomplishments in fertilizer production are also outstanding.[12] Speaking now in terms of nutrient value (i.e., approximately 23.3 per cent of gross fertilizer weight), estimates of production and capacity for N, $P_2O_5$, and $K_2O$ combined were 1,388,000 and 2,603,000 metric tons respectively in 1959–60 and 1,936,000 and 3,083,000 metric tons in 1965. Exports in 1959–60 totaled 360,000 metric tons.

[11] Ministry of Agriculture and Forestry, Japan, *Short History of Agricultural Development in Japan* (Tokyo, 1952), p. 16.
[12] *Far East Fertilizer Workshop,* Republic of China, Taipei, Taiwan, Oct. 24–Nov. 5, 1960, pp. 57, 107–108.

Even with the expansion of domestic consumption from an average 1,631,000 tons for the five-year period, 1955–59, to a post-1965 average which will exceed two million tons, a million or more tons will be available for export. Possibilities for such expansion exist. Trade discussions between Japan and Communist China in early 1963 reportedly involved the possible import by China of some 400,000 metric tons of chemical fertilizers.

## Comparisons of Fertilizer Use and Crop Yields

Certain ratios can be obtained for Communist China, Taiwan, and Japan if comparisons are made between the amount of available organic and chemical fertilizers per unit of cultivated land area and food crop hectares. The relevant data for 1956 are given in Table 2. The total availability of organic fertilizer per unit of food crop area is much larger in Japan and moderately higher in Taiwan than in Communist China. In both cases, a partial explanation may be found in the denser population and greater crop residues per unit of crop land in Taiwan and Japan. As a result of the greater supply of organic and chemical fertilizer per unit area, reinforced by other factors, food grain yields per crop hectare in Taiwan and Japan are about double that of mainland China. For 1956, indices of food grain crop yields for Taiwan and Japan (Communist China=100) are 197 and 229 respectively; for 1958, probably a year above average for China, the indices are 178 and 210 respectively (see Appendix Table 3). A part of the difference may be attributed to better natural conditions in Taiwan and Japan, including the availability of water that enables them to devote a much larger proportion of the food crop hectares to rice, which has a higher yield then upland grain. It is also possible that because of certain natural disadvantages in climate, topography, and availability of water, mainland China may not be able to equal the food grain yields of Japan and Taiwan, although she can improve her position considerably—even if chemical fertilizer is made available where it can be used effectively.

The data in Tables 1, 2, and 3 and Chart B provide a general illustration of the input of crop nutrients through organic and chemical fertilizer and the corresponding output of food grain per hectare. The yields are taken for 1956—a typical year for mainland China—at 1,471 kilograms per hectare for mainland China, 2,906 for Taiwan, and 3,369 for Japan. More recent yields in Taiwan and Japan have been much higher, as has the input of fertilizer. The basic differences in the ratios for the three areas are shown in the figures. The intake of nutrients in kilograms per hectare per metric ton of grain yield is taken at N, 30; $P_2O_5$, 12; and $K_2O$, 20 on the basis of various sources.[13]

It should be noted that certain points in the above calculations may appear inconsistent, and that the data used are subject to qualifications. Due to losses of N through leaching, which is partially or wholly offset by amounts gained through algae and small legumes in rice fields, it is difficult to strike a closely calculated balance of input and removal for this important crop nutrient. As for $P_2O_5$, there seems to be little doubt that it is being gradually depleted in the soils of China, even though some of its sources such as bones, ashes, etc., may not have been sufficiently accounted for. For Japan, the input of $P_2O_5$ and $K_2O$ seems excessive, but this may be partly due to some fixation in the soil while the extra amounts may make the total returns of all three crop nutrients more effective, thus resulting in gains in spite of the apparent excess.

The requirement of 59 million metric tons of increased food grain production in Communist China which will have

[13] Iso Eskichi, *Rice and Crops in Its Rotation in Sub-Tropical Zones* (Japan FAO Association, Tokyo, 1954).

TABLE 2. ESTIMATES OF AVAILABLE CHIEF PLANT NUTRIENTS FROM FERTILIZER IN COMMUNIST CHINA, TAIWAN AND JAPAN IN RELATION TO CROP AREAS AND FOOD PRODUCTION, 1956

| Units | Countries | | | Index | | |
|---|---|---|---|---|---|---|
| | China[1] | Taiwan[2] | Japan[3] | China | Taiwan | Japan |
| A. Organic Fertilizer (Thousand metric tons) | | | | | | |
| N | 3,809 | 40.0 | 347 | 100 | 1.05 | 9.1 |
| $P_2O_5$ | 1,741 | 21.3 | 140 | 100 | 1.22 | 8.0 |
| $K_2O$ | 3,235 | 31.6 | 285 | 100 | .98 | 8.8 |
| (Kg per hectare of cultivated land) | | | | | | |
| N | 34.0 | 45.7 | 60.8 | 100 | 134 | 179 |
| $P_2O_5$ | 15.5 | 24.3 | 24.9 | 100 | 157 | 161 |
| $K_2O$ | 29.3 | 36.1 | 50.0 | 100 | 123 | 171 |
| (Kg per hectare of food crops = .8 of total supply used on food crops)[4] | | | | | | |
| N | 24.6 | 30.4 | 45.6 | 100 | 124 | 185 |
| $P_2O_5$ | 11.2 | 16.2 | 18.7 | 100 | 145 | 167 |
| $K_2O$ | 21.0 | 24.0 | 37.4 | 100 | 114 | 178 |
| B. Chemical Fertilizer (Thousand metric tons)[5] | | | | | | |
| N | 178[6] | 63.6[5] | 407[5] | 100 | 357 | 229 |
| $P_2O_5$ | 25 | 24.6 | 292 | 100 | 98.4 | 1,168 |
| $K_2O$ | ... | 15.6 | 316 | ... | ... | ... |
| (Kg/per hectare of cultivated land) | | | | | | |
| N | 1.6 | 71.5 | 72.4 | 100 | 4,469 | 4,525 |
| $P_2O_5$ | 0.22 | 24.6 | 53.2 | 100 | 11,182 | 24,182 |
| $K_2O$ | ... | 15.6 | 55.8 | ... | ... | ... |

**(Kg/per hectare of food crops)**

| | | | | | | |
|---|---|---|---|---|---|---|
| N | 1.4 | 42.5 | 53 | 100 | 3,036 | 3,786 |
| P₂O₅ | .2 | 17.6 | 38 | 100 | 8,800 | 19,000 |
| K₂O | ... | 8.9 | 41 | ... | ... | ... |
| **Organic and Chemical (Kg/per hectare of cultivated land)** | | | | | | |
| N | 35.6 | 117.2 | 132.4 | 100 | 329 | 372 |
| P₂O₅ | 15.7 | 48.9 | 78.1 | 100 | 311 | 497 |
| K₂O | 29.3 | 51.7 | 105.8 | 100 | 176 | 361 |
| **(Kg/per hectare of food crop)** | | | | | | |
| N | 26.0 | 72.9 | 98.6 | 100 | 280 | 379 |
| P₂O₅ | 11.4 | 33.8 | 56.7 | 100 | 296 | 497 |
| K₂O | 21.2 | 32.9 | 78.4 | 100 | 155 | 370 |
| Food grain yield kg/hectare | 1,471 | 2,906 | 3,369 | 100 | 198 | 229 |
| Multiple crop index | 142 | 195 | 138 | | | |

[1] Estimated by the author. See Appendix Table 1, explanatory notes.
[2] Department of Agriculture, Taiwan.
[3] Minister of Agriculture, Tokyo.
[4] *Far East Fertilizer Workshop*, p. 116.
[5] Estimated by author at .7N, .8P₂O₅ and K₂O.
[6] Hong Kong Consulate General.

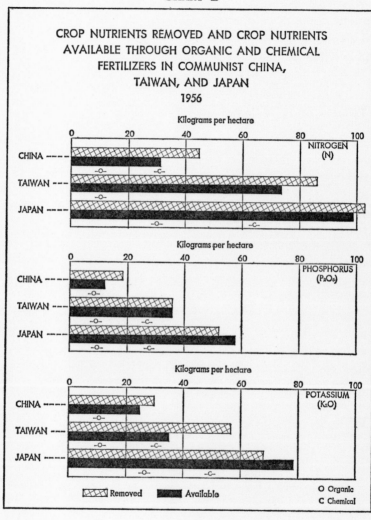

CROP NUTRIENTS REMOVED AND CROP NUTRIENTS
AVAILABLE THROUGH ORGANIC AND CHEMICAL
FERTILIZERS IN COMMUNIST CHINA,
TAIWAN, AND JAPAN
1956

to come from increased yields, as estimated later, would mean an increased requirement of 2.5 million metric tons of crop nutrients from chemical fertilizer, or about 20 kilograms per food crop hectare by 1972. Such an amount, even if available, would still leave input in China far below the present levels in Taiwan and Japan.

## IV. ESTIMATES OF FUTURE FOOD GRAIN AND FERTILIZER REQUIREMENTS IN COMMUNIST CHINA

Given the effect of chemical and organic fertilizer use in recent years and the inputs of crop nutrients compared with the output of food grain crops, we may now proceed to estimate the amount of chemical fertilizer needed by the crop year 1972–73. The year 1972 is taken as our target year for the following reasons:

1. It is 20 years after 1952 when, it is believed, agricultural production in Communist China once more approached the prewar level and the First Five Year Plan was about to be set in motion.

2. Chinese agriculture reached a major crisis in 1959–60 after 10 years of Communist management and, on the basis of current appraisal, it will take perhaps 10 more years before the necessary measures can be fully implemented in order to achieve production levels that are adequate for domestic and industrial purposes, without allowing for exports.

### Prewar Food Consumption Levels

According to certain continuing and still unpublished studies by Buck and Dawson, the prewar average (1931–37) production of "food grains and potatoes" was approximately 170 million metric tons. Allowing for change in stocks and assuming a prewar population level of 530 million for China

TABLE 3. ESTIMATES OF NUTRIENTS REMOVED BY CROPS (R) COMPARED
TO NUTRIENTS AVAILABLE (A) THROUGH ORGANIC AND CHEM-
ICAL FERTILIZERS (1956)

| Country | R Used by Crops | A Fertilizer Available Organic (O) Chemical (C) | | | Per cent Supplied by Fertilizer A/R |
|---|---|---|---|---|---|
| | Nitrogen (Kg/Hec) | | | | |
| | | O | C | Total | |
| China | 44 | 24 | 2 | 26 | 59 |
| Taiwan | 84 | 30 | 43 | 73 | 87 |
| Japan | 102 | 46 | 53 | 99 | 197 |
| | $P_2O_5$ (Kg/Hec) | | | | |
| China | 18 | 11.0 | 1.0 | 12 | 66 |
| Taiwan | 34 | 16.0 | 18.0 | 34 | 100 |
| Japan | 47 | 19.0 | 38.0 | 57 | 127 |
| | $K_2O$ (Kg/Hec) | | | | |
| China | 29 | 21.0 | — | 21 | 72 |
| Taiwan | 56 | 24.0 | 9.0 | 33 | 59 |
| Japan | 68 | 37.0 | 41.0 | 78 | 115 |

Total Input and Loss (Kg/Hec. of Food Crop Area)

| | Input (A) Organic | Chemical | Total | "Offtake" (R) | Per cent (A/R) |
|---|---|---|---|---|---|
| China | 56 | 3 | 59 | 91 | 65 |
| Taiwan | 70 | 70 | 140 | 174 | 80 |
| Japan | 102 | 132 | 234 | 217 | 108 |
| | | | Index | | |
| China | 100 | 100 | 100 | 100 | |
| Taiwan | 125 | 2,333 | 237 | 191 | |
| Japan | 182 | 4,400 | 397 | 238 | |

(including Manchuria and the outer provinces),[14] we may
put the gross production per capita at 321 kilograms. This
would be equivalent to 2,390 calories for all categories of
food and would seem to be fairly high, although grossly uneven distribution acted as an offseting factor.

The rounded gross figure of 300 kilograms per capita is

[14] For the ratio of net food grain to food grain available, see Shen, op.
cit., Appendix Table 4.

equivalent to 196 kilograms of net food available at a conversion rate of 0.653.[15] The daily caloric intake available would be 2,180 per capita for all food, which is slightly above 2,054 calories for a well balanced diet set by the Chinese Medical Association in 1939. It also compares favorably with the corresponding figure in most underdeveloped countries, but in some 5 per cent short of the 2,314 and 2,310 calories officially reported for Taiwan and Japan, respectively, in 1958.

Although the rate of population increase may fluctuate considerably, a net annual rate of about 2 per cent in the next 10 years seems more likely if the trend of economic improvement observed in 1952–58 is restored. On the other hand, population pressure on the land and the periodic occurrence of poor grain crops, together with other unpredictable depressant factors or a definite and successful government policy to hold down the birth rate, could conceivably lower the rate to only 1.5 per cent. Unless conditions become very disrupted and some very poor crop seasons occur, it would seem most unlikely that the rate could level off to 1 per cent. At a growth rate of 2 per cent, the 1972 population would be in the neighborhood of 882 million.

The estimated food grain requirement would then be close to 264 million metric tons. This would, in turn, require an increase in production of some 74 million metric tons over the 1962 level, not allowing for possible exports.

This increase in available supply would have to come mainly from: (1) expanded area in food crops; (2) improved agricultural techniques interacting with (3) increased available plant nutrients through the application of organic and chemical fertilizers.

---

[15] Both higher and lower population estimates for the prewar period are available. The exact number remains a moot point. The essential point, however, has to do with the per capita availability of food which can be checked against the prewar rural dietary survey.

## Potential Increase from Acreage Expansion

As far as an expansion of the area in crops is concerned, the potential is limited inasmuch as there is already an extreme pressure on the land. Further expansion in double cropping is also limited due to lack of water. In fact, a sizeable portion of the present cultivated area now in crops is not suitable for economic operation.

There are some divergent opinions on this matter. According to Shen (*op. cit.* p. 363), for instance, most of the arable land suitable for expansion is in Manchuria, and, while the area under wheat and cotton could be expanded moderately, that planted to rice might profitably be reduced. It is possible that the production of wheat and other food grains in North China could be expanded significantly if water were available.

James Thorp, on the other hand, believes that cultivation in the rice region could be expanded materially if fertilizer were available at economic rates.[16] Furthermore, the Communist Chinese could bring a great deal of idle land into cultivation through heavy applications of dolomitic limestone, which is in ample supply, as well as fertilizer that is high in nitrogen, phosphorus, and potassium content. Thorp also feels reasonably sure that some soils will need the application of minor elements and that on the good soil of the wheat region, yields could be increased considerably by the use of fertilizer and by extension of irrigation.

Large areas in China that once were under cultivation have been abandoned as a result of erosion. It is possible that with great effort and expense, some of this land can be brought back into the production of food crops, although most of it should perhaps be put into trees and grass. The

[16] James Thorp (author of *Geography of Soils of China*): note to the writer.

latter measure would be helpful to the general food and fuel situation without adding directly to the food grain crops. Nevertheless, extensive areas may be reclaimed by irrigation, drainage, and desalinization; a plan to reclaim 30 million hectares in 15 years has been referred to by Mao.[17] However, only some two million hectares were reclaimed during the First Five Year Plan, while reliable reports on increases since then are not available. It is not known how the estimate of 30 million hectares was arrived at, but the figure is also confirmed by Kovda, an eminent Soviet soil scientist, who for some time worked with Chinese specialists in Communist China.[18]

In view of the preceding discussion and with due allowance for some uneconomic lands which should be taken out of cultivation, we may hazard a generous estimate that food crop hectares could be increased by a net figure of ten million hectares in the next ten years if a tremendous, concentrated effort is made in both the reclamation of saline and waterlogged areas and irrigation. If, through improved techniques, an average yield of 1,500 kilograms per hectare could be attained on such lands—this would be higher than the prewar average of 1,454 and about equivalent to the 1956 level—the production gain would be 15 million metric tons. This would leave another 59 million metric tons to be de-derived from increased yields.

## Potential Increase in Production from Greater Yields

As noted in Table 3, some 40 to 50 per cent of the fertilizer inputs applied in Japan and Taiwan come from organic fertilizer. With an active program of chemical fertilizer pro-

[17] Gyan Chand (Indian economist), *Factual Account of the New Economy of China—Analysis and Interpretation* (Bombay: Vora, 1958), p. 108.
[18] V. A. Kovda (Soviet soil scientist), *Soils and the Natural Environment of China* (Moscow: U.S.S.R. Academy of Science, 1959). English translation, U.S. Joint Publications Research Service, Washington, D. C., p. 12.

duction in mainland China, we can perhaps assume that by 1972 the source of crop nutrients to increase yields may be supplied by organic and chemical fertilizer in about equal proportions. This assumption also seems to check roughly with the expected increase in supplies available in the next decade from night soil, animal manure, and other organic sources and with the expected greater success in conserving the available elements in organic manure.

If we follow Richardson's and other estimates on the effect of improved agricultural techniques, including improved varieties, crop rotation, water conservation, and so forth, when carried out in conjunction with adequate chemical fertilizer supply, the following percentage increases in yield may be assumed:

From organic fertilizer, 40 per cent

From chemical fertilizer, 40 per cent

From improved techniques, 10 per cent

Of the required 59 million metric tons of increase in food grain from higher yields, about 24 million metric tons are thus assumed to come from chemical fertilizer and an equal amount from organic fertilizer, while 11 million metric tons may be ascribed to improved techniques.

At the ratio of roughly 1 million metric tons of gross chemical fertilizer to 2 million metric tons in yield (a ratio of about 1:8 for plant nutrients) of food grain, some 12 million metric tons of chemical fertilizer would be needed at about the ratio of N-3, and $P_2O_5$ and $K_2O$ together—2, in equivalent amounts of gross fertilizer, i.e., ammonium sulfate, calcium, superphosphate, and potassium sulfate or chloride. For the other nonfood grain crops, including cotton, fruit, vegetables, and so forth, another 3 million metric tons of gross chemical fertilizer would be needed, making a total of 15 million metric tons gross or some 3.4 million metric tons of crop nutrients (N, $P_2O_5$ and $K_2O$) at a ratio of 4.4:1.0.

## Comparison with India and Taiwan

It may be of interest to compare the calculations of chemical fertilizer needs in India and Taiwan with those of mainland China derived above. According to Parker,[19] India's Third Five-Year Plan calls for an increase of some 31.1 million metric tons of food grain crops over the 1956–58 average of 68.9 million metric tons. The chemical fertilizer requirements for all crops were calculated at 1.28 million metric tons of plant nutrients. If about 80 per cent were used on food crops, the requirement would be 1.02 million metric tons which should produce 7.8 million metric tons of food grains. "This indicates that about 25 per cent of the planned increase might be the direct result of the use of fertilizer and 75 per cent from irrigation, good seeds, pest control and other improved practices." Parker apparently also includes the use of available organic manure under "other improved practices." The 1962 study of the National Council of Applied Economic Research for India, on the other hand, indicates a somewhat greater requirement for chemical fertilizer in relation to production goals for food grain crops, while attributing a lesser proportion to other factors.[20]

In the case of Taiwan, the increased use of 500,000 metric tons of gross chemical fertilizer on paddy rice between 1945–46 and 1958–59 was associated with the production increase of 1,550,000 metric tons of rice. On the basis of experimental data, about 60 per cent of the increase may be attributed directly to chemical fertilizer, leaving 40 per cent to other

[19] F. W. Parker (Assistant Director General, Technical Department, FAO), *Fertilizers and Economic Development* (Rome, Feb. 1962), pp. 21–22.
[20] National Council of Applied Research, New Delhi, *Long Term Projections of Demand and Supply of Selected Agricultural Commodities, 1960–61 to 1975–76*, pp. 128–36.

factors. As Taiwan's use of improved techniques was already far advanced, she needed more chemical fertilizer per unit of output than mainland China and India where improved techniques were less advanced and the potential increase in yield from this factor, when more chemical fertilizer is also applied, could be greater. Thus, according to the method developed above in estimating mainland China's need for chemical fertilizer for food grain crops by 1972, only about 40 per cent of the increase in yields is attributed to chemical fertilizer; 60 per cent must be attributed to other factors including organic fertilizer and improved techniques.

### The Estimated Shortfall in Fertilizer Production and Its Effect

Most recent reports from China forecast for 1963 a chemical fertilizer production of only 2.6 million metric tons as compared with 2.18 in 1962.[21] At this rate of increase, the increase in productive capacity for the 1972–73 crop production would equal only 3.4 million metric tons in eight years' time. The above estimate thus allows for doubling the present annual increased rate.

Even if her progress were greatly accelerated, bearing in mind that one to two years are needed to erect new plants, one might put Communist China's maximum production of chemical fertilizer by 1972 at 7.5 million metric tons. This would exceed the present production of chemical fertilizer in Japan and is about 3.5 times the production of Communist China in 1962 after 13 years of developmental effort.

If the domestic production of chemical fertilizer were to attain a level at most of 7.5 million metric tons per year by the 1972–73 crop year, the following results may be set forth on the basis of the assumption of respective annual population growth rates of 2 per cent and 1.5 per cent respectively.

[21] U.S. Consulate-General, Hong Kong.

|  | 2 per cent Increase | 1.5 per cent Increase |
|---|---|---|
| 1. Population, millions | 882 | 826 |
| 2. Total food grain available based on 7.5 (15–7.5) million metric tons [shortfall in] chemical fertilizer production, million metric tons | 234 | 234 |
| 3. Gross food grain available per capita, kilograms | 265.3 | 283.3 |
| 4. Food, net (3 x 0.653)* per capita, kilograms | 173.3 | 185.0 |
| 5. Daily caloric availability, calories | 1,638 | 1,749 |
| 6. All food (5÷0.85), calories | 1,927 | 2,058 |
| 7. Minus 5 per cent—during poor crop years, calories | 1,831 | 1,955 |
| 8. Minimum adequate level, calories | 2,180 | 2,180 |

* Shen, *op cit.*, Appendix Table 4.

In a poor crop year, food production may fall 5 to 10 per cent below average but is likely to be partly balanced by some use of food stocks. See Chart C.

If one assumes that only 7.5 million metric tons of chemical fertilizers will be available at the beginning of the 1972–73 crop year and the respective population increases of 2 per cent and 1.5 per cent, the required production of food grains may be compared with the amount available as follows: [22]

|  | Model A 2 per cent Population Growth | Model B 1.5 per cent Population Growth |
|---|---|---|
|  | *Million Metric Tons* | |
| Required | 262.0 | 248.0 |
| Available | 234.0 | 234.0 |
| Shortfall | 28.0 | 14.0 |
| Fertilizer imports needed | | |
| For food grain production | 6.0 | 3.0 |
| For other crops | 1.5 | .7 |

[22] If, in the 1953 Census there was actually an undercount of 3 to 7.5 per cent, as some students of Chinese population growth believe, it would be necessary to raise the national minimum food requirements for 1972 proportionally above the figures shown above by as much as 10 to 20 million metric tons. This would present an even more difficult situation.

There are alternative methods of calculating the effect of a shortfall in chemical fertilizer. The above projections are admittedly conservative. They assume a much greater input to agriculture than has been the practice in the past ten years, as well as the adoption by Communist China of certain improved methods that must be predicated upon a substantial shift of government support to agriculture and a revival of production incentives set back by mismanagement in the communes. Besides, both changes must be made on a long-term basis. However, even the attainment of a food grain production of 234 million metric tons by 1972 with the use of 7.5 million metric tons of chemical fertilizer would be a noteworthy achievement only when compared with the 1962 level of about 190 million metric tons. Even during the good years under the Communist regime, i.e., from 1952 to 1957, food grain production did not increase more than 2.5 million metric tons annually.

In the event of a shortfall in Communist China's chemical fertilizer production, it would be much cheaper to import fertilizer than food grains. The present ratio between the two imports is about 45 to 70 in favor of fertilizer so that import of fertilizer, when other factors for increasing production are also present, can result in an increase in yield at considerably less than one half the cost. At previous prices, the shortfall in grain indicated in Model A above would cost some 2 billion dollars; the corresponding cost in Model B would be 1 billion dollars. In addition to the high cost, it would obviously be impossible to take any major portion of such quantities from the world's exportable surplus. But even to import the necessary amount of chemical fertilizer would constitute an undue drain on foreign exchange which is largely derived from export of agricultural products. Besides, the introduction of such a large import demand for chemical fertilizer, even if it could be satisfied, would have a material impact on world supplies and prices.

According to the FAO, international trade in chemical fertilizer nutrients (N, $P_2O_5$, and $K_2O$) in 1958–59 reached nearly 6.5 million metric tons and was increasing at the rate of 2 per cent per year.[23] Since the rate of increase was expected to accelerate, it could well reach, or even exceed, 9 million metric tons by 1972. Should Communist China's import requirements reach 7.5 million metric tons gross, or more than 1.5 million metric tons of plant nutrients, some 16 per cent of the world's exportable surplus would be involved. During the same period, the import demand from other countries undoubtedly will also have greatly risen. The question is, will the exporting countries be willing and able to expand their capacity to produce chemical fertilizer in anticipation of Communist China's rising demand?

Perhaps Communist China is seeking to solve her problem by accelerating domestic chemical fertilizer production to a greater extent than has been assumed. If this is the case, she may have certain difficulties in obtaining an adequate supply of all the required raw materials. A tremendous development in hydroelectric power will help to supply the nitrogen needed. The situation, however, is less favorable with respect to phosphate. As stated by Shen (*op. cit.,* p. 36), the phosphate deposits for manufacturing fertilizer as determined about 1946 by the National Geological Survey of China showed an estimated amount of only some 47,586,000 metric tons which would last only a few years at the rate of estimated future requirement. Furthermore, much of the phosphate deposits is located in remote areas, and transportation to manufacturing centers would be costly. Since the above Survey, the Communists have found more extensive and accessible sources of lower grade phosphate that could be used, given the processing and transportation facilities. On the other hand, potassium does not pose as great a problem.

[23] FAO, *Fertilizers, Annual Review of World Production, Consumption and Trade* (Rome, 1960), p. 23.

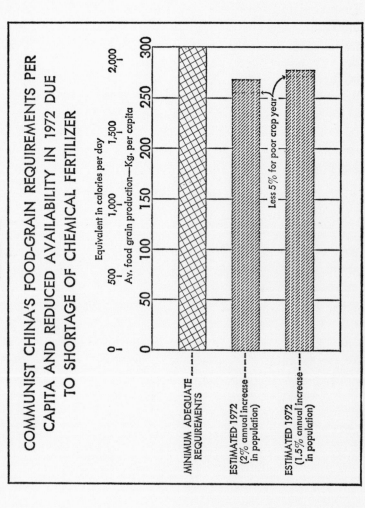

CHART C

COMMUNIST CHINA'S FOOD-GRAIN REQUIREMENTS PER CAPITA AND REDUCED AVAILABILITY IN 1972 DUE TO SHORTAGE OF CHEMICAL FERTILIZER

Equivalent in calories per day

Av. food grain production—Kg. per capita

MINIMUM ADEQUATE REQUIREMENTS

ESTIMATED 1972 (2% annual increase in population)

ESTIMATED 1972 (1.5% annual increase in population)

Less 5% for poor crop year

Potassium is more plentiful than phosphate in the soils of China and exists in fairly large supply in Chekiang Province.

Apart from the question of raw materials, the problem of financing and operating the new fertilizer plants is tremendous. So is the double task of assembling the raw materials for an immense fertilizer industry and of distributing the fertilizer, whether produced at home or imported, to tens of millions of farms. The tonnage to be moved over long distances by water, rail, and trucks would claim a large part of the country's transport capacity, and, since the work would be beyond the capacity of human carriers, it would require the building of a network of new, improved, and extended highways.

## V. SUMMARY

Communist China's food grain production has not kept pace with the needs of a large and increasing population. If she cannot build up her food grain production to the level of minimum nutritional requirements in the next ten years, malnutrition will be a serious problem in ordinary years; in bad years, widespread famine will result.

Communist China has tried to accelerate the process of extending improved methods of agricultural production— such as improved seed, insect and disease control, improved methods of plowing, and irrigation management—which was already under way on clearly marked lines during the Nationalist regime. Some attention has also been given to the need for more chemical fertilizer, but the progress achieved falls far short of the country's need.

The apparent failure of agriculture in mainland China to meet food crop production requirements when weather conditions are adverse over large areas and other conditions are also unfavorable has demonstrated to the Communist officials the weakness of their agricultural policy. Drastic measures will be necessary in order to bring food production into line with the population. Chief among these measures are a greatly increased availability of chemical fertilizer and a greatly increased supply of water. From reports available to date, there is no clear evidence that the responsible officials are laying out an effective program to meet these needs.

Potential expansion in food crop area is limited and depends much on major developments in irrigation. Reclamation itself can provide only a limited increase in food crop areas.

The main increase in production must come from increased yields which basically depend on the use of more fertilizer. Increase in organic fertilizer is to a large extent a function of the increase not only in human and animal population but crop residues as well. But within such a closed cycle it is not possible to meet the need for more crop nutrients without bringing in substantially more chemical fertilizer.

With the most generous allowance for increase in yields due to improved agricultural techniques and use of organic fertilizer, Communist China will still require a minimum of 15 million metric tons of chemical fertilizer a year by the middle 1970's, unless the rate of population increase declines considerably. It seems impossible for Communist China to produce the required chemical fertilizer, and—if it were produced—to distribute it effectively. The result would seem to be a heavy shortfall in food production, especially in bad weather cycles, with severe economic consequences.

## APPENDIX

### Comparative Data on Fertilizer Use

Table 2 shows the amount of chief crop nutrients (N, $P_2O_5$, and $K_2O$) used per cultivated land and food crop area in mainland China, Taiwan and Japan. Although data for

1956 and 1958 are both available, 1956 is taken as a more normal year for China and the statistical data are also more dependable.

Comparisons with Taiwan and Japan are particularly useful as there are long series of recorded data in both cases which show heavy dependence on organic fertilizer (See Table 3 and Appendix Table 2). For 1956, the ratio of organic fertilizer to total estimated fertilizer used was as follows:

|  | $N$ | $P_2O_5$ | $K_2O$ |
|---|---|---|---|
|  | *Per cent* | | |
| Taiwan | 41 | 47 | 73 |
| Japan | 47 | 33 | 47 |

For mainland China, almost all the added crop nutrients came from organic fertilizer, but no official figures were issued on the amounts supplied by different items. Some acceptable estimates based on extensive research are shown in Appendix Table 1 and Charts D and E. Eight items are covered in these estimates, which probably present a more comprehensive picture than is available in other published sources.

Although some of the items are different for Taiwan and Japan, the totals cover essentially the same items and the proportions coming from animal manure, night soil, and compost compare fairly closely.

Total crop nutrients available from organic fertilizer per food crop hectare are larger in Taiwan and Japan. In both cases, higher yields result in the return of more organic residues to the soil. In 1956, Japan imported substantial amounts of food grains while grains were exported from Taiwan. This would account for some of the difference in available residues.

The same proportionate availability of animal manure was

CHART D
# COMMUNIST CHINA: SOURCES OF ORGANIC
## FERTILIZER, 1956

GROSS WEIGHT

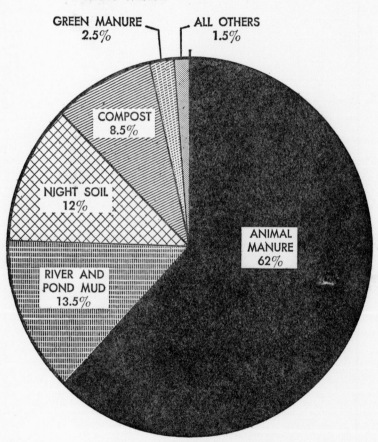

GREEN MANURE
2.5%

ALL OTHERS
1.5%

COMPOST
8.5%

NIGHT SOIL
12%

RIVER AND
POND MUD
13.5%

ANIMAL
MANURE
62%

1,314,967,000 METRIC TONS

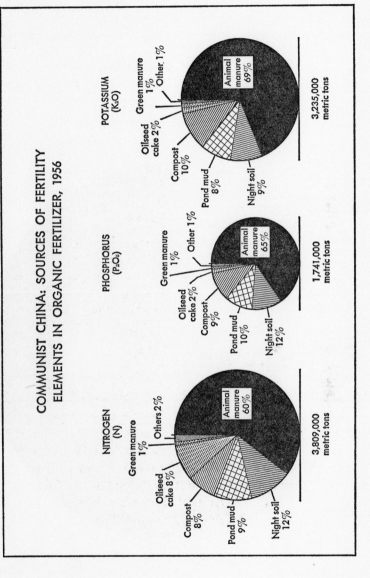

COMMUNIST CHINA: SOURCES OF FERTILITY
ELEMENTS IN ORGANIC FERTILIZER, 1956

NITROGEN
(N)

Green manure 1%

Others 2%

Oilseed cake 8%

Compost 8%

Pond mud 9%

Night soil 12%

Animal manure 60%

3,809,000 metric tons

PHOSPHORUS
(P₂O₅)

Green manure 1%

Other 1%

Oilseed cake 2%

Compost 9%

Pond mud 10%

Night soil 12%

Animal manure 65%

1,741,000 metric tons

POTASSIUM
(K₂O)

Green manure 1%

Other 1%

Oilseed cake 2%

Compost 10%

Pond mud 8%

Night soil 9%

Animal manure 69%

3,235,000 metric tons

used for all three countries. However, since the manure was more efficiently used in Taiwan and Japan, the amount actually available per hectare, compared with mainland China, might be greater than shown. The reverse may be true in the case of night soil.

APPENDIX TABLE 1. COMMUNIST CHINA'S FERTILIZER SITUATION, 1956
(IN THOUSAND METRIC TONS)

| | Gross | N | Per cent | $P_2O_5$ | Per cent | $K_2O$ | Per cent |
|---|---|---|---|---|---|---|---|
| I 1) Chemical fertilizer[1] | 1,500 | | | | | | |
| Nitrogenous (85 per cent) | 1,275 | 255 | 20.0 | — | — | — | — |
| Phosphatic (15 per cent) | 255 | — | — | 36 | 14.0 | — | — |
| II Organic Fertilizer | | | | | | | |
| 2) Animal manure | 815,367 | | | | | | |
| At 70 per cent available | 570,756 | 2,283 | 0.4 | 1,142 | 0.2 | 2,283 | 0.3 |
| 3) Night Soil | 156,000 | | | | | | |
| At 60 per cent available | 93,100 | 468 | 0.5 | 187 | 0.2 | 280 | 0.3 |
| 4) Oil seed cakes | 6,000 | | | | | | |
| At 70 per cent available | 4,200 | 294 | 7.0 | 42 | 1.0 | 63 | 1.5 |
| 5) Green manure | 30,000 | | | | | | |
| At 80 per cent available | 24,000 | 48 | 0.2 | 12 | 0.05 | 36 | 0.15 |
| 6) Compost | 116,000 | | | | | | |
| Plant residues, etc. at 70 per cent available | 81,000 | 324 | 0.4 | 162 | 0.2 | 324 | 0.4 |
| 7) River and pond mud | 180,000 | | | | | | |
| At 80 per cent available | 144,000 | 360 | 0.25 | 180 | 0.13 | 217 | 0.15 |
| 8) Others | 11,600 | | | | | | |
| At 10 per cent of item available | 8,120 | 32 | 0.4 | 16 | 0.2 | 32 | 0.4 |
| O.M. total | 1,314,967 | | | | | | |
| Per capita | 2,104 | 3,809 | | 1,741 | | 3,235 | |
| Per crop hectare 8.2 metric tons | | | | | | | |

[1] U.S. Consulate-General, Hong Kong, 1959.

### Explanatory Notes

*Animal manure.* Livestock figure from *The Great Ten Years* converted to animal units—116,481,000. Manure calculated at 7 metric tons per animal unit based on estimates from various sources. Buck, *Land Utilization,* p 238. Iso, *op. cit.,* pp. 245-47 (*op. cit.,* see note 13). 70 per cent calculated as available (Iso, *op. cit.,* p. 248). Per cent elements: N-.4, P₂O₅-.2, K₂O-4, based on Scott,* p. 153, and Iso, *op. cit.,* p. 246.

*Night soil.* Figured at .25 metric ton per capita, based on *Land Utilization* data; also Shen, *op. cit.,* p. 33. Placed between Japan, which seems high, and Taiwan, which appears low. 60 per cent available. Scott, *op. cit.,* p. 69, places loss from cities at about 50 per cent. As the loss in the country should be less, average availability is placed at 60 per cent.

*Oil seed cakes.* T. H. Shen (*Agricultural Resources of China,* p. 34) estimated China's prewar oil seed cakes production as about 5,800,000 metric tons, consisting of cakes and meals from soybean, peanuts, rapeseeds, cottonseeds, sesame seeds, tea seeds and tungnut seeds, etc.

With the extension of oil-crop areas and the general efforts to expand the application of oil cakes as fertilizers in 1956, the amount available for fertilizer that year may be roughly estimated as 6,000,000 metric tons, with soybean cakes constituting about 66 per cent of the total, or 4,000,000 metric tons. (The figure quoted officially as distributed.)

Estimates Nutrient Content from Oil Seed Cakes, 1956 **

| | | $N$ | $P_2O_5$ | $K_2O$ |
|---|---|---|---|---|
| a) | Soybean cakes: | | | |
| | Per cent of content | 7.5 | 1.0 | 1.5 |
| | Amount of content (metric tons) | 300,000 | 40,000 | 60,000 |

* James Cameron Scott, *Health and Agriculture in China,* Russel Square London: 1942.
** National Central University (Nanking), 1934 experiments, gave the nutrient content as follows:

| | $N$ (percent) | $P_2O_5$ (percent) | $K_2O$ (percent) |
|---|---|---|---|
| a) Soybean cakes | 7.67 | 1.10 | 1.58 |
| b) Rapeseed cakes | 5.05 | 2.00 | 1.30 |
| Cottonseed cakes | 6.06 | 2.25 | 1.18 |
| Sesameseed cakes | 5.86 | 3.27 | 1.45 |
| Tung-nut cakes | 5.99 | 2.10 | 1.20 |
| b) Other cakes: | $N$ | $P_2O_5$ | $K_2O$ |
| Available per cent of content | 5.5 | 2.0 | 1.2 |
| Amount of content | 11,500 | 40,000 | 28,000 |
| Total amount of (a) and (b) | 410,000 | 80,000 | 88,000 |

Availability placed at 70 per cent, the same as barn manure which may be high for nitrogen with usual practices of handling.

*Green manure.* Estimate based on *Rice and Crops,* F.A.O. Association, Tokyo, 1954, and Wang Chi-ming, "Strenuous Accumulation and Rational Application of Fertilizers," *New China Semi-Monthly,* No. 24, December 1957. "China now has only 3,200,000 hectares of green manure," according to the last source. We extend it to 6,666,000 hectares in 1962. Per unit yield is rather low at 11.25 MT/Hec, and we intend to raise it to 22.50 in 1962. We have taken 3,000,000 hectares at 10 MT per hec. There are no data on availability which is assumed to be 80 per cent. Iso, *op. cit.,* p. 215, shows a lower figure. Per cent of nutrients based on Chiao Shen-huei, "The Three Nutrients in Farm Manures" (*Agricultural Science Bulletin,* No. 5 [May 6, 1956] pp. 273-76), and Iso, *op. cit.,* p 257, ("Fertilizer Ingredients of Green Manure Crops").

*Compost, plant residues, etc.* Iso, *op. cit.,* p. 269, states: "Bedding material in case of cattle equals 4.5 kg. (about 1.6 metric tons annually) per A.U." For China we consider one

Notes to Appendix Table 1 (*Continued from page 139*)

ton for barn and outdoor compost ample due to less availability of litter material and plant residues. Iso (p. 269) gives analyses of barn compost at N-0.6 per cent, $P_2O_5$-0.5 per cent and $K_2O$-0.8 per cent, which is higher than that shown on page 251, and the percentages used in reports of the Taiwan and Japan M.O.A.F. Following a study of these data we tentatively use the following percentages: N-0.4, $P_2O_5$-0.2, and $K_2O$-0.4 or the same as those used for animal manure, excepting $K_2O$. In case much chemical fertilizers is used with the outdoor compost, this might be somewhat on the low side. At 116 million animal units at 1 metric ton per animal unit $=$ 116 million tons. Assuming 70 per cent availability which may be high for nitrogen $=$ 81 million metric tons at N, 0.004$=$324,000 metric tons; $P_2O_5$, 0.002$=$162,000 metric tons; $K_2O$, 0.004$=$325,000 metric tons.

*Pond mud, etc.*

1. River mud and pond mud usually are heavy in weight and contain very low percentages of soil nutrient elements. There are only two types of farms which could use mud or mire with much advantage: (a) those farms which are situated quite close to rivers or canals, or having convenient access to some lakes or ponds; and (b) those farms raising high-priced cash crops, such as cotton, tobacco, sugar cane, mulberries, etc.

2. As a result of these cost factors, river mud and pond mud are not used very extensively as fertilizers except in the following regions: (a) the Yangtze Delta region which possesses a large canal system where muds are rich with organic matter and water transport is cheap, and where mulberry, cotton and tobacco are produced in considerable quantities; (b) the Pearl River Delta, which also provides cheap water transportation with its riverlets and canals, and where mulberry and sugar cane crops require large amounts of fertilizers; and (c) certain cotton and tobacco areas in the North China plain, where the farms have easy access to rivers, canals, or ponds may also use mud as subsidiary fertilizing agents; the application here, however, is much less extensive than in the Yangtze or Pearl River deltas.

3. Of China's total cultivated area, we estimate about 10 million hectares may use 8 metric tons per hectare (those areas mentioned above), and about 50 million hectares may use 2 metric tons per hectare. Since these muds are locally collected and locally applied within a short distance, farmers under Communist directives could report exaggerated figures in order to satisfy the authorities. This seems a very high estimate; actual application is very hard to check.

4. Basing estimates at 8 metric tons per hectare for 10 million hectares and 2 metric tons per hectare for 50 million hectares, the total amount of river mud and pond mud applied in China would reach an impressive total of 180,000,000 metric tons.

5. The Communist estimate (Wang Chi-ming, *op. cit.*) of nutrient content for river mud and pond mud is:

$$N = \frac{1\text{-}4}{1,000}; \quad P_2O_5 = \frac{1}{1,000}; \quad K_2O = \frac{1\text{-}2}{1,000}$$

If we take the average of N$=$0.26 per cent; $P_2O_5$$=$0.1 per cent; $K_2O$$=$0.15 per cent, the 180,000,000 metric tons of mud at 80 per cent available or 144,000,000 metric tons would contain in thousand metric tons: N, 288; $P_2O_5$, 144; $K_2O$, 216.

6. "Others" include such items as ashes, street debris, stalks, leaves, bones, floor and chimney sweepings, etc., and is roughly placed at 10 per cent of the value of compost.

APPENDIX TABLE 2. OFFICIALLY REPORTED ORGANIC FERTILIZER SUPPLIES IN 1956 ADJUSTED FOR AVAILABILITY
(IN THOUSAND METRIC TONS)

### Taiwan

| | Gross | N | Per cent | $P_2O_5$ | Per cent | $K_2O$ | Per cent | Per cent Available | N | Adjusted $P_2O_5$ | Adjusted Amounts $K_2O$ |
|---|---|---|---|---|---|---|---|---|---|---|---|
| Animal manure | 2,530 | 7.6 | .30 | 3.8 | .15 | 2.5 | .10 | .70 | 5.3 | 2.7 | 1.8 |
| Night soil | 1,652 | 8.3 | .50 | 4.1 | .25 | 8.2 | .50 | .60 | 5.0 | 2.5 | 4.9 |
| Green manure | 1,544 | 7.7 | .50 | 1.5 | .10 | 7.7 | .50 | .80 | 6.1 | 1.2 | 6.1 |
| Compost | 7,327 | 30.7 | .42 | 15.4 | .21 | 11.0 | .15 | .70 | 21.5 | 10.8 | 7.7 |
| Straw | 560 | 3.2 | .57 | 1.3 | .23 | 5.9 | 1.05 | .70 | 2.1 | .9 | 4.1 |
| Ash | 257 | - - | | 4.3 | 1.7 | 8.7 | 3.4 | .90 | - - | 3.9 | 7.8 |
| Total | 13,870 | 57.5 | | 30.4 | | 44.0 | | | 40.0 | 22.0 | 32.4 |
| Per capita | 1.321 M.T. | | | | | | | | | | |
| Per crop hectare | 8.87 M.T. | | | | | | | | | | |

### Japan

| | Gross | N | Per cent | $P_2O_5$ | Per cent | $K_2O$ | Per cent | Per cent Available | N | Adjusted $P_2O_5$ | Adjusted Amounts $K_2O$ |
|---|---|---|---|---|---|---|---|---|---|---|---|
| Animal manure | 49,002 | 247.5 | .50 | 131.3 | .27 | 242.4 | .495 | .70 | 173.2 | 91.9 | 169.7 |
| Night soil | 26,935 | 137.9 | .51 | 27.2 | .11 | 62.6 | .23 | .60 | 82.7 | 16.3 | 37.5 |
| Green manure | 8,343 | 41.8 | .50 | 9.8 | .12 | 36.5 | .44 | .80 | 33.4 | 7.8 | 29.2 |
| Others | 8,631 | 82.2 | .95 | 33.5 | .39 | 68.8 | .80 | .70 | 57.5 | 23.5 | 48.2 |
| Total | 92,911 | 509.4 | | 201.8 | | 410.3 | | | 346.8 | 139.5 | 284.6 |
| Per capita | 1.032 M.T. | | | | | | | | | | |
| Per crop hectare | 11.2 M.T. | | | | | | | | | | |

Sources: 1. *Taiwan Agricultural Year Book*, Provincial Department of Agriculture.
2. Japan *Ministry of Agriculture and Forestry Year Book*.
3. Same adjustment as for China. See Appendix Table 1, Explanatory notes.

APPENDIX TABLE 3. CALCULATED AVAILABLE CHIEF FERTILIZER ELEMENTS IN COMMUNIST CHINA, TAIWAN, AND JAPAN IN RELATION TO CULTIVATED LAND AND FOOD CROP AREAS AND PRODUCTION DATA, 1958

| Units | Countries | | | Index | | |
|---|---|---|---|---|---|---|
| | China[1] | Taiwan[2] | Japan[3] | China | Taiwan | Japan |
| **1,000 MT Organic Fertilizer Total Available Supplies** | | | | | | |
| N | 4,615 | 43.5 | 362.7 | 100 | .94 | 7.86 |
| $P_2O_5$ | 2,084 | 24.4 | 142.9 | 100 | 1.17 | 6.86 |
| $K_2O$ | 3,253 | 35.1 | 295.8 | 100 | 1.08 | 9.09 |
| **Kg/Hec of Cultivated Land** | | | | | | |
| N | 42.7 | 49.1 | 58.9 | 100 | 115 | 138 |
| $P_2O_5$ | 19.3 | 27.8 | 23.2 | 100 | 144 | 120 |
| $K_2O$ | 30.0 | 40.5 | 49.2 | 100 | 135 | 164 |
| **Kg/Hec of Food Crops (.8 of total supply used on food crops)[4]** | | | | | | |
| N | 30.5 | 33.0 | 48.3 | 100 | 117 | 172 |
| $P_2O_5$ | 13.8 | 18.0 | 19.0 | 100 | 143 | 151 |
| $K_2O$ | 21.5 | 26.6 | 39.4 | 100 | 111 | 164 |
| **1,000 Metric Tons of Chemical Fertilizer Total Available[5] (.7N, .8 P and K)** | | | | | | |
| N | 321.0[6] | 71.4[5] | 415.1[5] | 100 | 22.24 | 129 |
| $P_2O_5$ | 57.0 | 27.0 | 292.8 | 100 | 47.37 | 514 |
| $K_2O$ | . . . | 21.4 | 308.8 | . . . | . . . | . . . |
| **Kg/Hec of Cultivated Land** | | | | | | |
| N | 3.0 | 81.1 | 67.0 | 100 | 2,703 | 2,233 |
| $P_2O_5$ | .5 | 30.8 | 44.9 | 100 | 6,160 | 8,980 |
| $K_2O$ | . . . | 24.0 | 50.5 | . . . | . . . | . . . |

| | | | | | | |
|---|---|---|---|---|---|---|
| **Kg/Hec of Food Crops** | | | | | | |
| N | 2.1 | 47.3 | 55.3 | 100 | 2,252 | 2,633 |
| P₂O₅ | .45 | 18.6 | 39.0 | 100 | 4,133 | 8,666 |
| K₂O | ... | 12.1 | 41.0 | ... | ... | ... |
| **Organic and Chemical Kg/Hec Cultivated Land** | | | | | | |
| N | 45.7 | 130.2 | 125.9 | 100 | 285 | 275 |
| P₂O₅ | 19.8 | 58.6 | 68.1 | 100 | 296 | 344 |
| K₂O | 30.0 | 64.5 | 99.7 | 100 | 215 | 332 |
| **Organic and Chemical Kg/Hec of Food Crop Area** | | | | | | |
| N | 32.6[1] | 80.3[2] | 103.6[3] | 100 | 246 | 318 |
| P₂O₅ | 14.2 | 36.6 | 58.0 | 100 | 258 | 408 |
| K₂O | 21.5 | 38.7 | 80.4 | 100 | 180 | 374 |
| **Food Grain Yield** | | | | | | |
| Kg/Hec (1958) | 1,737 | 3,092 | 3,645 | 100 | 178 | 210 |
| Double Cropping Index | 150 | 195 | 137 | 100 | 130 | 91 |

[1] Estimated by the author. See Appendix Table 4.
[2] Department of Agriculture, *Taiwan Year Book*, 1958.
[3] Minister of Agriculture, Tokyo, *Statistical Year Book*, 1959.
[4] *Far East Fertilizer Workshop*, p. 116.
[5] Estimated by the author.
[6] American Consulate General, Hong Kong, for total.

APPENDIX TABLE 4. COMMUNIST CHINA'S AVAILABLE FERTILIZER, 1958
(IN THOUSAND METRIC TONS)

| | Gross | Per cent | N | Per cent | $P_2O_5$ | Per cent | $K_2O$ |
|---|---|---|---|---|---|---|---|
| I 1) Chemical | 2,700 | | | | | | |
| Nitrogenous 85 per cent and 20 per cent | 2,295 | 20 | 459 | .. | ... | .. | ... |
| Phosphatic | 405 | .. | ... | 20 | 81 | .. | ... |
| II Organic | | | | | | | |
| 2) Animal Manure Available | 1,056,000 | | | | | | |
| 70 per cent | 739,200 | .4 | 2,957 | .2 | 1,478 | .3 | 2,318 |
| 3) Night soil Available | 164,500 | .5 | | | | | |
| 60 per cent | 98,700 | .5 | 493 | .2 | 197 | .3 | 296 |
| 4) Oil Seed Cakes Available | 7,000 | | | | | | |
| 70 per cent | 4,900 | 7 | 343 | 1.0 | 49 | 1.5 | 74 |
| 5) Green Manure At 80 per cent Available | 35,000 | | | | | | |
| | 28,000 | .2 | 56 | .05 | 14 | .15 | 42 |
| 6) Compost, Plant Residues, etc. 70 per cent Available | 132,000 | | | | | | |
| | 92,400 | .4 | 369 | .2 | 184 | .4 | 370 |
| 7) River and Pond Mud At 80 per cent Available | 180,000 | | | | | | |
| | 144,000 | .25 | 360 | .10 | 144 | .15 | 216 |
| 8) Others At 10 per cent of "6" | 13,200 | | | | | | |
| | 9,240 | .4 | 37 | .2 | 18 | .4 | 37 |
| O. M. Total Gross | 1,587,700 | | 4,615 | | 2,084 | | 3,253 |
| Per Capita | 2,406 kg. | | | | | | |
| Per Crop Hec. | 10.16 kg. | | | | | | |

*Explanatory Notes*

Although 1958 was not a typical year, the data in Tables 3 and 4 are included primarily for illustration. The data on areas are from official sources. The figure for 1958 population is based on calculations of the U.S. Census Bureau based on certain assumptions. The most important point is the increase in animal units reported by Communist sources. We question this increase. As the calculations of organic manure are to a large extent functions of the human and animal population, the increases shown for China may be considered optimistic owing to the high animal unit data. The increase in yield (kilogram per hectare) of food crops, abstracted from inaccurate reporting, is also only in part due to increased availability of fertilizer elements and must be ascribed to the favorable weather and, to a moderate extent, to improved agricultural techniques. An estimate of 210 million metric tons production for 1958 is used instead of the 250 million metric tons, the officially recorded figure.

Other outstanding points between the two years' data are explained below:

1. Data from official source through the U.S. Consulate General in Hong Kong. The data in the chemical fertilizer total is reduced by the factors 0.7 for N and 0.8 for P and K to allow for losses in use. As factors of "availability" are used for organic fertilizer, it is considered that some allowance for losses should also be used for chemical fertilizer to make totals of the elements available for the three areas more comparable. The factors are subject to correction.

2. Official figures on livestock used due largely to reported increases in hogs. The number seems much too high, and there has certainly been a decline since then in view of the food shortage and falling-off of exports. The same factors are used for nutrients as in Table 1; $K_2O$ at 0.4 is higher than used in Taiwan but is well supported.

3. See explanatory notes from Table 1.

4. A total increase in the gross quantity of oil cake is shown and availability of the fertilizer elements placed at 70 per cent, or the same as for animal manure. Two-thirds of the cake used are estimated as from soybeans. Per cent content of soybean cake; N, 7.5, $P_2O_5$, 1.0, and $K_2O$, 1.5 as shown in Appendix Table 1, Explanatory Notes.

5. Green manure is moderately increased but not up to the plan stated by Wang Chiming (*op. cit.*, p. 2, Explanatory Notes, Appendix Table 1). The value of green manure for $P_2O_5$ and $K_2O$ is open to question. It is placed at N, .2 per cent, $P_2O_5$, .05 per cent, and $K_2O$, .15 per cent, following the figures used by Chiao Shen-huei. (Explanatory Notes, Appendix Table 1.) These figures differ from those used in Taiwan and Japan official statistics, which run about 1.5, 0.10 and 1.5 respectively. The mainland China figures seem too high and may have to be revised downward.

6. This item is substantially increased along with the animal units shown at 132 million metric tons. (See discussion in Appendix Table 1, Explanatory Notes.)

7. This is retained at the same figure as for 1956. For explanation of method used in estimate, see this item in Table 1, Explanatory Notes.

8. Calculated in the same way as for 1956, i.e., at 10 per cent of item 6.

APPENDIX TABLE 5. OFFICIALLY REPORTED ORGANIC FERTILIZER SUPPLIES 1958[1]
ADJUSTED FOR AVAILABILITY. 1,000 METRIC TONS

**Taiwan[1]**

| | Gross | N | Per cent | $P_2O_5$ | Per cent | $K_2O$ | Per cent | Adj. Factor | N | $P_2O_5$ | $K_2O$ |
|---|---|---|---|---|---|---|---|---|---|---|---|
| Animal manure | 2,920 | 8.8 | .30 | 4.4 | .10 | 2.9 | .10 | .70 | 6.1 | 3.1 | 2.0 |
| Night soil | 2,000 | 10.0 | .50 | 5.0 | .25 | 10.0 | .50 | .60 | 6.0 | 3.0 | 6.0 |
| Green manure | 1,224 | 6.2 | .50 | 1.2 | .10 | 6.1 | .50 | .80 | 5.0 | 1.0 | 4.9 |
| Compost | 7,759 | 32.6 | .42 | 16.3 | .21 | 11.6 | .15 | .70 | 22.8 | 11.4 | 8.1 |
| Straw | 594 | 3.4 | .57 | 1.4 | .23 | 6.2 | 1.05 | .70 | 2.4 | 1.0 | 4.3 |
| Ash | 324 | ... | ... | 5.4 | 1.70 | 10.9 | 3.4 | .90 | ... | 4.9 | 9.8 |
| Total | 14,821 | 61.0 | ... | 33.7 | ... | 47.7 | ... | ... | 42.3 | 24.4 | 35.1 |
| Per capita | 1.420 MT | | | | | | | | | | |
| Per crop hectare | 9.88 MT | | | | | | | | | | |

**Japan[2]**

| | Gross | N | Per cent | $P_2O_5$ | Per cent | $K_2O$ | Per cent | Adj. Factor | N | $P_2O_5$ | $K_2O$ |
|---|---|---|---|---|---|---|---|---|---|---|---|
| Stable manure A.U. 5.014M 9.8 MT per AU | 49,140 | 251.8 | .51 | 133.6 | .27 | 246.6 | .50 | .70 | 176.3 | 93.5 | 172.6 |
| Night Soil 0.3 percent | 27,540 | 152.0 | .55 | 30.4 | .11 | 69.9 | .25 | .60 | 91.2 | 18.2 | 41.9 |
| Green manure | 10,820 | 54.1 | .50 | 12.6 | .12 | 47.2 | .44 | .80 | 43.3 | 10.1 | 37.8 |
| Others | 7,810 | 74.2 | .95 | 30.2 | .39 | 62.1 | .80 | .70 | 51.9 | 21.1 | 43.5 |
| Total | 95,310 | 532.1 | ... | 206.8 | ... | 425.8 | ... | ... | 362.7 | 142.9 | 295.8 |
| Per capita | 1.380 MT | | | | | | | | | | |
| Per crop hectare | 11.6 MT | | | | | | | | | | |

[1] Department of Agriculture, Taiwan, for totals.
[2] MOAF Tokyo, for totals.

APPENDIX TABLE 6. CHEMICAL FERTILIZER SUPPLIES
Japan 1955-56

|   |   | $N$ | $P_2O_5$ | $K_2O$ |
|---|---|---|---|---|
|   |   | | (1,000 Metric Tons) | |
| 1) | Total | 567 | 365 | 395 |
| 2) | Available | 407 | 292 | 316 |
| 3) | Food crops | 326 | 234 | 253 |
|   |   | | (Kg/Hec) | |
| 4) | (3) ÷ 6 million | 54 | 39 | 42 |
|   |   | | 1957-58 | |
|   |   | | (1,000 Metric Tons) | |
|   |   | 593 | 367 | 386 |
|   |   | 415 | 293 | 309 |
| 3) | F. C. | 332 | 234 | 247 |
|   |   | | (Kg/Hec) | |
| 4) | (3) ÷ 5.98 million | 55.5 | 39 | 41 |

[1] *Far East Fertilizer Workshop,* Table 5, p. 56.
[2] Tentatively in stated amt. available for plant use N, .7; P2O5 and K2O, .8.
[3] Calculated at .8 from data in *Far East Fertilizer Workshop.*
[4] See Table 2, Food Crop Area, MOAF. *Statistical Year Book,* 1958, December 1959.


APPENDIX TABLE 7. CHEMICAL FERTILIZER SUPPLIES, 1956
Taiwan

|   |   | $N$ | $P_2O_5$ | $K_2O$ |
|---|---|---|---|---|
|   |   | | (1,000 Metric Tons) | |
| 1) | Total | 90.8 | 30.7 | 19.5 |
| 2) | Available | 63.6 | 24.6 | 15.6 |
| 3) | Food crops | 44.8 | 18.6 | 9.4 |
|   |   | | (Kg/Hec) | |
| 4) | 3 ÷ 1.054M | 42.5 | 17.6 | 8.9 |
|   |   | | 1958 | |
|   |   | | (1,000 Metric Tons) | |
| 1) | Total | 102.1 | 34.1 | 26.7 |
| 2) | Available | 71.4 | 27.0 | 21.4 |
| 3) | Food crops | 50.0 | 19.6 | 12.8 |
|   |   | | (Kg/Hec) | |
| 4) | 3 ÷ 1.050M | 47.6 | 18.7 | 12.2 |

[1] Table 2, *Far East Fertilizer Workshop,* p. 73.
[2] Calculated at N, .7; P2O5 and K2O, .8.
[3] For food crops N, .7; P2O5, .8; K2O, .6.
[4] See Table 3 for sources of area and other data. *Taiwan Agriculture Year Book,* 1962 edition.

APPENDIX TABLE 8. SOIL FERTILITY ELEMENTS REMOVED Per
METRIC TON OF FOOD GRAIN IN KILOGRAMS

|  | $N$ | $P_2O_5$ | $K_2O$ |
|---|---|---|---|
| 1)  Rice | 30 | 14 | 20 |
| 2)  Wheat | 28 | 11 | 14 |
| 2)  Maize | 28 | 10 | 20 |
| 2)  Barley | 25 | 10 | 20 |
| Factor used for all food grains | 30 | 12 | .20 |
| Total Removed per hectare based on 1956 yields (Table 1) | | | |
| China | 1,471 | 44 | 18 | 29 |
| Taiwan | 2,906 | 87 | 35 | 58 |
| Japan | 3,369 | 101 | 40 | 67 |

[1] Iso, *op. cit.*, pp. 211, 214.
[2] Miller and Turk, *Soil Science*, pp. 314-16.

OWEN L. DAWSON

# Irrigation Developments Under the Communist Regime

## I. BACKGROUND

Communist China's need for enormous amounts of chemical fertilizer is covered in the paper on fertilizer requirements. Outside the paddy rice area, however, only a limited portion of the food grain crops can at present make economical use of chemical fertilizer without irrigation. It is particularly pertinent at this time, therefore, to examine the reports on mainland China's progress in expanding irrigation and her future targets in that direction.

China has been noted through the centuries for the great and ingenious efforts put forth by her rulers and farmers to conserve and use available water. The prodigious work of constructing terraces and of storing, diverting, and even carrying water long distances for growing crops has impressed observers from other countries. However, more organized effort has been needed to control and use available water sources efficiently over the country and adapt crops to seasonally available supplies. Likewise, more technical and scientific information has been required to utilize the potentials of water conservancy fully. This has included the cost of pumping, management of key pumping stations, the maintenance of diversion canals, and tests on water quality.

A growing awareness of these needs was shown by China's

national authorities in the 1930's, and plans were initiated to carry out several important projects. These works included the organization of six Water Conservancy Bureaus under the Ministry of Water Conservancy. The Hwai River project for drainage and irrigation, the Yangtze Gorge project, and general plans for the Yellow River were set forth. Extensive work was begun on local improvement projects with the aid of bank loans made to cooperatives. A study of undeground water resources of the North China plain was made by the eminent geologist, Wong Wen-hao.

Continuation of these projects and studies was seriously affected by the war, but was actively resumed in 1946. In two years, projects covering about 0.5 million hectares were underway with funds borrowed from the Farmers Bank of China. The damage due to the war required a vast amount of work repairing dykes for flood control.

Communist China emphasized the continuation and expansion of all the above projects—especially flood control and prevention—during the First Five-Year Plan (1953–57). A rather ambitious plan was set forth to expand the irrigated area by four million hectares by 1957; this is an area equivalent to the combined size of New Hampshire and Vermont. The importance of accumulating hydrographic information and basic surveys with overall long range water conservation research was emphasized. The close coordination of water conservation measures with industrial, agricultural, and communications development together with an overall study of the requirements of flood prevention, irrigation, hydroelectric power, and navigation was also recognized. A tremendous further expansion by some 40 per cent was envisioned in the goal for 1967.

This report is a commentary on officially reported figures on areas under irrigation and includes statements by officials and specialists on the effectiveness of irrigation and the problems involved in expanding the area. A summary of projects for future expansion is given with detailed appendices on source material. An endeavor is made to estimate the increase in effectively irrigated area since the Communist takeover and the general potentiality of future irrigation. Tables 1 and 2 provide official figures and derived calculations on areas irrigated; Table 3 lists annual irrigation developments reported by the *Hydro-electricity* research staff according to type of project; and Table 4 gives data on the 1958 plan conservancy targets by province and type of project.

## II. EXPLANATION OF THE TERM "IRRIGATION"

To understand the Communist Chinese statistics on irrigated cultivated land it is important to know what land has been included under the term "irrigation."

The Chinese term of *kwan kai* for irrigation refers to the application of water to fields. The word *kwan* is used in China whenever water is put into a container, i.e., *kwan shui* (putting water into a container). The word *kai* means "to irrigate." When water is put on a field, the soil is the container; in the case of rice fields with raised borders, the field is the container. Thus, the terraced rice fields, as in Szechwan, which are not planted to winter crops for the purpose of retaining precipitation to conserve enough water for the summer crop of rice, may be considered as a form of irrigation, since it is an act of "containing" water. The different methods used in irrigation and the proportion of localities using each method are tabulated in Table 16, p. 168, of *Land Utilization in China—Statistics*[1] (hereafter referred to as *LU-B*).

Traditionally, the Chinese classify cultivated land into paddy fields, dry fields, and dry fields irrigated, as has been

[1] John Lossing Buck, (A) *Land Utilization in China* (Chicago: University of Chicago Press; Nanking, China: University of Nanking, 1937 [out of print]); (B) *Land Utilization in China—Statistics* (Chicago: University of Chicago Press, 1937 [out of print]).

done by the Communists (Table 2, items 2 and 4). The term
"paddy fields" refers to fields growing rice. The term paddy
(Malay: *padi*) refers to rice in the husk, growing or harvested. Hence, the term should include upland rice as well
as rice grown in water. If this definition were adhered to, it
would conflict with the term "dry fields" because upland
rice is grown in dry fields. It appears possible that with usage
in China, paddy fields have come to mean rice fields where
rice is grown in water. It is clear in Table 2, item 2, that the
category paddy fields (irrigated) excludes upland rice.

The next semantic problem is that of types of rice land
included under the term "irrigated." It seems probable that
low land with field boundaries and naturally under water
would be included as irrigated. Areas under deep water,
where a deep water variety of rice is grown, might not have
been included since there are no visible field boundaries.
These areas are very small in relation to the total area in rice.
Fields not planted to winter crops for the purpose of retaining precipitation during the winter season are probably included as irrigated paddy fields, since rice is grown in water
conserved for that purpose.

## III.  COMPARATIVE IRRIGATION STATISTICS

Three Chinese Communist sources of statistics on annual
amounts of irrigated land for 1949–56 list significantly different figures (Table 2, items 5, 6, and 7). Even what appears to be the most reliable source, item 5, begins with 26
million hectares irrigated in 1949 and ends with 37.6 million
hectares in 1956—an incredible increase of 11.6 million hectares irrigated. The 1949 figure as given in *The Great Ten
Years* [2] is only 16 million hectares and increases to 32 million
in 1956 and to 66.7 million in 1958. The latter figure when

[2] *Economic and Cultural Statistics of Communist China (The Great Ten
Years)*, State Statistical Bureau, Peking, Feb. 2, 1960.

TABLE 1. COMPARATIVE STATISTICS ON IRRIGATED LAND IN MAINLAND
CHINA FOR THE PRE-COMMUNIST AND COMMUNIST PERIODS

| Sources | Total Cultivated Land *(in million hectares)* | Irrigated Land *(in million hectares)* | Per Cent of Cultivated Land |
|---|---|---|---|
| A. Pre-Communist period | | | |
| 1. *Statistical Monthly,*[a] 1929–32 | 76.7 | 18.6 | 24.2 |
| 2. (Adjusted basis "3" cultivated area) | 102.4 | 24.8 | 24.2 (25) |
| 3. *Land Utilization in China,*[b] 1929–33, for 22 provinces plus Sikang, Sinkiang, and Manchuria | 102.4 | 40.3 | 39.4 |
| B. Communist period | | | |
| 1. State Statistical Bureau,[c] 1949 | 97.9 | 26.0 | 27.0 |
| 2. State Statistical Bureau,[c] 1956 | 111.8 | 37.6 | 33.6 |
| 3. Water Conservancy,[d] 1958 | 107.8 | 66.7 | 61.9 |
| (adjusted)[d] | | 37.6 | 34.9 |
| 4. Krylov,[e] 1957 | 111.8 | 39.8 | 35.6 |

Notes to Table 1

[a] The *Statistical Monthly* (see note 7). The areas are given in *mow* and have been converted to hectares by multiplying by the conversion factor of 6.144 mow per acre, as given in the *Monthly*. The data omit two provinces, Tsinghai and Kwangsi, and a number of *hsien* in other provinces and, therefore, do not represent the total area, or the area irrigated—particularly because Kwangsi has a high proportion of irrigated land. If included, 25 per cent might be the more probable proportion irrigated. The amounts for both cultivated land and irrigated land are too low because of unregistered land and are adjusted as shown.

[b] *Land Utilization in China* (see note 1). Study on irrigation includes statistics on irrigation for 16,456 farms, 164 localities, 22 provinces, China (1929–33). The crop area irrigated is 45.8 per cent of the total crop area, p. 214, Table 12, of the *LU-Statistical* volume. The percentage of 45.8 multiplied by the 88 million.

[c] *Economic and Cultural Statistics of Communist China,* p. 120 (see note 2).

[d] See note c, Table 2.

[e] See note e, Table 2.

adjusted for error would probably not be greater than 37.6 million hectares. The adjustment is made by adding 2.9 million hectares (a portion of the 1958 goal) to the 1957 amount of 34.7 million hectares. All three sources give great increases in 1956 over 1955, which may be considered in part statistical increases for partial correction of understated amounts for earlier years and an increase due to inclusion of the existing irrigated areas where irrigation systems were reported as improved. Evidence of the latter point is the quotation from the *Handbook of Agricultural Statistical Work* that follows. None of the sources indicate as high an amount irrigated as the 40.3 million hectares irrigated in 1929–53, see Buck, *LU-B* (Table 1).

*The Handbook of Agricultural Statistical Work* states:

The increased area of irrigation is the actual area of irrigation expanded during the period of report through various measures, such as the popularization of the experience of the scientific control of use of the water and improving the management of the irrigation system, and the construction of the new and the repair of the old irrigation works (or equipment). It also includes the area of farm land which could be effectively irrigated following the completion of repairs to irrigation works but, due to certain reasons such as lack of rainfall, irrigation was not carried out. In order to correctly record the work in the paddy rice growing districts of the south and to satisfy the needs of plans and work, the statistics for the irrigation area should comprise, apart from "the non-irrigated land turned into irrigated fields," the item "single-crop rice turned into double-crop rice." The increased area of irrigation would be computed on the basis of the cultivated area, of land and not the sown area. Therefore, in filling the questionnaires, the dry land (land dependent on rainfall) which has been turned into irrigated land for paddy field, should be placed under the term of "non-irrigated land turned into irrigated land," while the originally irrigated single-crop rice field which has been turned into double-crop rice field (not including the irrigated land on which are grown only additional minor spring crops, such as rape seed or the growing of a stubble crop such as stubble rice) would be placed under "single-crop rice turned into double-crop rice." However, in the yearly report summing up the total expansion of irrigated land, the increased irrigation area should be only the area of "non-irrigated land turned into irrigated field," and not the total of the above two figures.[3]

[3] *Handbook of Agricultural Statistical Work* (Peking: Statistical Publishing House, June 1956).

This definition sets forth specific directions for the areas to be reported. If double cropping of rice land had been previously counted as two hectares, the 1956 data would show a decrease rather than an increase, except for the fact that the directives provided for the inclusion of improvements in existing irrigated areas. This factor plus a possible attempt to correct understated amounts for previous years may account for the big jump in 1956 [4] (see Tables 2 and 3). Exaggerated reports to show that the set goals had been attained, or surpassed, may be another factor in the large increase. This does not mean that from 1955 to 1956 there was no increase in the amount of area irrigated; it merely emphasizes the probability of underestimates in earlier years. Unfortunately, there appears to be no way of determining the extent to which the effective irrigated area may have been increased.

Computations from M. M. Krylov's [5] statement that 84 per cent of the water is used for rice (see Table 1, note[e]) yield a total irrigated area of 39.8 million hectares in 1957, or 0.5 million fewer hectares than the 40.3 million in 1929–33 (see Buck, *LU-B*, Table 12, p. 124).

In North China one would expect a continuation of the trend of increase in percentage of area irrigated in the wheat region as reported in *LU* for 38 localities—from 11.9 per cent in 1904–09 to 13.5 per cent for 1914–19, to 15.3 per cent for 1924–29 up to 16.6 per cent in 1929–33 (see *Economic and Cultural Statistics*,[6] Table 17, p. 188). Column V of Table 3 lists increases from wells, waterwheels, and river pumps, a large proportion of which probably occurred in North China. The large increase in 1956 is, of course, unrealistic.

There is no doubt but that great efforts were made to in-

[4] *Hydro-electricity* (Technical Periodical), No. 4, (April 1957).
[5] M. M. Krylov, *Brief Review of the Underground Water of Communist China* (Tashkent: U.S.S.R., Academy of Science, 1958). Trans. by U.S. Publishing Research, Washington, D. C., p. 4.
[6] *Op. cit.*, note 2.

TABLE 2. COMPARATIVE DATA ON LAND USE AND IRRIGATION IN MAINLAND CHINA, 1949–58
(IN MILLION HECTARES)

| Items by sources of data | 1949 | 1950 | 1951 | 1952 | 1953 | 1954 | 1955 | 1956 | 1957 | 1958 |
|---|---|---|---|---|---|---|---|---|---|---|
| A. *Economic Statistical Abstract:* | | | | | | | | | | |
| 1. Cultivated land, total[a] | 97.9 | 100.4 | 103.7 | 107.9 | 108.5 | 109.4 | 110.2 | 111.8 | 111.8 | 108.7 |
| 2. Irrigated paddy fields[a] | 22.8 | ... | ... | 25.9 | 26.0 | 26.3 | 26.5 | 27.4 | ... | ... |
| 3. Land in dry fields, total[a] | 75.1 | ... | ... | 82.0 | 82.5 | 83.1 | 83.7 | 84.4 | ... | ... |
| 4. Irrigated dry fields[a] | 3.2 | ... | ... | 4.9 | 5.0 | 5.3 | 5.6 | 10.2 | ... | ... |
| 5. Irrigated land (Item 2 plus item 4) | 26.0 | ... | ... | 30.8 | 31.0 | 31.6 | 32.1 | 37.6 | ... | ... |
| B. *Hydroelectricity:* | | | | | | | | | | |
| 6. Irrigated land[b] | 20.2 | 20.8 | 21.8 | 23.4 | 24.0 | 24.8 | 26.1 | 36.0 | 38.3 | ... |
| C. *Water Conservancy:* | | | | | | | | | | |
| 7. Irrigated land[c] | 16.0 | 16.7 | 18.7 | 21.3 | 22.0 | 23.3 | 24.7 | 32.0 | 34.7 | 66.7 (37.6) |
| 8. Crop hectares in rice[d] | 25.7 | 26.1 | 26.9 | 28.4 | 28.3 | 28.7 | 29.2 | 33.3 | 32.2 | 32.7 |
| D. Krylov[e] | | | | | | | | | 39.8 | |

Notes to Table 2

a *Economic Statistical Abstract,* State Statistical Bureau, February 1960, p. 120.

b "Statistical Data of China's Irrigated Area in Recent Years," *Hydro-electricity,* no. 7 (April 11, 1957).

c *Shui-li Shui-tien Chien-she* (Water Conservancy and Hydro-electric Construction), No. 18, 1959, p. 55. As possible clue to the exaggerated 66.7 million hectares for 1958, a quotation from *Teng Tsu-hui* (Chinese Youth) Jan. 1, 1959, may help: "Of the cultivated area of the country, one-third has good irrigation facilities or very poor facilities." Thus, two-thirds of the total cultivated area of 107.8 million hectares for 1958 gives 66.7 million hectares irrigated. Perhaps a mistake was made in stating the proportions as for total cultivated area, rather than for the proportion of total irrigated area.

The target figure in "The 1958 Plan Targets for Water Conservancy in China," published in *Water Conservancy in China* No. 9 (Sept. 14, 1957) and compiled by the editorial staff gives targets of 2.9 million hectares of new irrigated area, 2.9 million hectares of irrigated area to be improved, and 3.2 million hectares to be drained. If it is assumed that the 34.7 million hectares of irrigated land in 1957 were increased by 2.9 million hectares, the 1958 figure would be 37.6 million hectares, a very generous assumption, but a more rational amount than 66.7 million hectares.

d *Economic and Cultural Statistics of Communist China* (The Great Ten Years), p. 120. (see note 2).

e M. M. Krylov, *Brief Review of the Underground Water of Communist China* (see note 5) states that 84 per cent of the irrigation water is used for rice. The Communist claim of 32.3 million crop hectares in rice in 1957 reduced by the *Land Utilization in China* (see note 1) amount of 3.4 million hectares double cropped, considering interplanting of early and late rice as 1 hectare rather 2 hectares, equals 28.9 million hectares of rice land. Computations from the *LU* study give 93.6 per cent of rice land as irrigated. Thus, the irrigated rice land in 1957 may be considered as 27 million hectares irrigated. If all other crops used the same amount of water per crop hectare as rice, the total number of hectares irrigated would be 32.1 million (28.9 million divided by 84 per cent of water for rice), of which 5.1 million would be for crops other than rice. If other crops used only 40 per cent as much water as rice, 12.8 million hectares of other crops may be considered as irrigated. The sum of 27 million plus 12.8 million equals 39.8 million hectares of cultivated irrigated land.

crease the irrigated area. Rather, the question is one of effectiveness attained. Chinese engineers state that water from some of the projects never reached the farmer's land and that in other cases salinity and waterlogging developed. The mismanagement mentioned by Krylov may also apply to many existing projects. The changes in farm organization from the family farm to Agricultural Producers Cooperatives and then to Communes may have upset the established management of irrigation systems by introducing new systems of "mismanagement." This may have occurred quite widely and resulted in decreased effective irrigation in such areas. The Communist irrigation figures for 1958 are lower than the 40.3 million hectares in 1919–33 from the *LU* figures given in item A (2) in Table 1, or the 39.8 million hectares computed from Krylov's statement that 84 per cent of the water is used for rice. To some extent this may be due to differences in land included as irrigated. However, they are much higher than the adjusted pre-war figures from the *Statistical Monthly*.[7]

Despite the difficulty of proving increases in effective irrigation—a vast and complicated subject because of the lack of precise definitions—it is the belief of many analytical observers both in Washington and Hong Kong as well as such specialists as Dr. Wu [8] that the tremendous efforts expended on irrigation works resulted in a significant increase in the irrigated area, at least in the early stages. On the other hand, it is possible that some of the post-1956 floods [9] may have been partly caused by ill-considered construction of canals. As a result of the calamitous period, 1959–62, the entire program has to come up for review.

## IV. EFFECTIVENESS OF IRRIGATION PROJECTS

In view of the extravagant claims of the Communists' reports on land placed under irrigation, an illuminating comment was made by the Vice Minister of Water Conservancy [10] —namely, that of 34.7 million hectares (see Table 2) reported under irrigation in 1957, 10.1 million or 29.1 per cent were incapable of resisting drought.

In the 1957 conference on water conservancy work, Ho Chi-fun gave the following brief summation: (1) Up to 1957 [11] some 30.5 per cent of the nation's cultivated land of 112 million hectares was well provided with irrigation of one sort or another. (2) There were still 40 million hectares

[7] Directorate of Statistics, National Government *Statistical Monthly* (Nanking), combined issues for Jan. and Feb. 1932.

[8] Yuan-li Wu, *An Economic Survey of Communist China* (New York: Bookman Associates, 1956), pp. 323–36 and 338–39.

[9] Chu-yuan Cheng, *Communist China's Economy, 1949–1963* (Seaton Hall University Press, 1963), p. 143.

[10] *Chinese Water Conservancy*, Nov. 9, 1957.

[11] *Ibid.*, Sept. 14, 1957.

TABLE 3. AREAS ATTRIBUTABLE TO VARIOUS IRRIGATION WORKS AND FACILITIES
(MILLION HECTARES)

| | I Irrigation Added in Recent Years[a] | II Cumulative Area under Irrigation | III Large Scale Projects under State Budget | IV Cooperative Projects of Medium Small Scale | V Irrigation Wells, Water Wheels, and River Pumps |
|---|---|---|---|---|---|
| 1949 | | 20.2 | 1.6 | 17.4 | 1.2 |
| 1950 | 0.6 | 20.8 | 1.7 | 17.7 | 1.3 |
| 1951 | 1.0 | 21.8 | 1.8 | 18.4 | 1.6 |
| 1952 | 1.6 | 23.4 | — | — | — |
| 1953 | 0.6 | 24.0 | 2.0 | 19.2 | 2.1 |
| 1954 | 0.8 | 24.8 | 2.2 | 20.4 | 2.2 |
| 1955 | 1.3 | 26.1 | 2.4 | 21.2 | 2.5 |
| 1956 | 9.9 | 36.0 | 2.8 | 25.8 | 7.4 |
| 1957[b] | 2.3 | 38.3 | — | — | — |
| 1958 | — | — | — | — | — |
| 1959 | — | — | — | — | — |

*Comments:* The above table is compiled by the research staff of the Chinese periodical, *Hydro-electricity,* on the basis of official data; it seems to be the work of technicians. The area under irrigation begins with a higher figure in 1949 and runs higher than the data put out later in *The Great Ten Years.* (See note 2).

[a] "Statistical Data of China's Irrigated Area in Recent Years," *Hydro-electricity* (Chinese, semi-monthly), No. 7 (April 11, 1957).

[b] The 1957 figure of irrigation area is taken from the *Chinese Daily,* based on reports through December.

suitable for irrigation, which should be gradually supplied in successive five-year plans. (3) In an ordinary year, about 6 million hectares scattered over the country are vulnerable to flood or waterlogging, usually at five-year intervals. These hectares can be saved only by an extensive system of river control and drainage over a period of several decades.

A basic limitation on water resources for irrigation was pointed out by the Chief Soviet Expert, Korniev, at the National Conference on Water Conservancy and Hydro-electric Power in 1959.[12] Korniev stated that China has an annual supply of 2,680 cubic kilometers of water, some 500 of which were used for irrigation in 1959, and he estimated a potential need by 1960 of 700–800 cubic kilometers. While it was observed that the total supply was apparently sufficient for

[12] *People's China,* No. 20, 1957.

meeting potential demand, the distribution was considered very uneven.

Korniev thought the Yellow River, the Hwai River, the Hai River, and the Liao River valleys were particularly short of moisture. This cotton-wheat belt is fast running out of water resources, and any further development of water resources in the near future must depend to an important extent on underground water, deep wells, and water pumps—all of which are also limited. He made an extended and basic statement on the results of water conservancy work in 1958. In deference to published statements on the remarkable accomplishments reported in 1958, Korniev added, "You all know of these achievements; they have been mentioned in various reports. It is difficult to do them full justice." He then went on with incisive critical comments to the effect that general plans were being drawn up for most of the larger rivers but that they were just beginning to show something of

> . . . the specifications and arrangement of the order of sequence in the construction of the projects. Yet as technical planning documents they fail to reflect in their entirety the changes which have taken place in agriculture, water conservancy construction, and electric power industry.
>
> In the rural areas vast changes have taken place in conditions of direct flow as a result of the energetic construction of mass water conservancy projects and that therefore major amendments have to be made in respect to hydrological calculations. The existing plans make no allowance for decrease in water quantity and a change in the equilibrium which is taking place and will continue to in the next two or three years.[13]

With regard to the large number of water conservancy projects built in 1958, Korniev considered their usefulness to depend mainly on correct management:

[13] *Ibid.*

TABLE 4. THE 1958 PLAN TARGETS FOR WATER CONSERVANCY
IN MAINLAND CHINA

| | Irrigation Area to be Added (10,000 mow) | Irrigation Area to be Improved (10,000 mow) | Area to be Drained (10,000 mow) | Soil and Water Conservation (sq. km.) |
|---|---|---|---|---|
| Total* | 4,386 (29.2 Million hectares) | 4,373 | 4,817 | 48,523 |
| Hopei | 547.5 | 100.0 | 1,450 | 6,000 |
| Shansi | 100.0 | 97.0 | — | 6,400 |
| Inner Mongolia | 200.0 | — | 1.5 | 2,700 |
| Liaoning | 90.0 | 30.0 | 300.0 | 3,200 |
| Kirin | 135.0 | — | 120.0 | 2,000 |
| Heilungkiang | 200.0 | 22.5 | 225.0 | 150 |
| Shensi | 120.0 | — | 20.0 | — |
| Kansu | 100.0 | 26.0 | 4.0 | 10,000 |
| Chinghai | 16.0 | 4.0 | — | — |
| Sinkiang | 156.0 | 20.0 | — | — |
| Shantung | 400.0 | 500.0 | 410.0 | 1,250 |
| Kiangsu | 200.0 | 400.0 | 670.0 | 200 |
| Anhwei | 101.6 | 110.0 | 95.1 | 400 |
| Chekiang | 40.0 | 500.0 | 50.0 | 300 |
| Fukien | 50.0 | 80.0 | 36.0 | 100 |
| Honan | 554.0 | — | 303.9 | 5,890 |
| Hupei | 80.0 | 525.0 | 996.0 | 4,000 |
| Hunan | 40.0 | 800.0 | 20.0 | 300 |
| Kiangsi | 150.0 | 250.0 | 15.0 | 400 |
| Kwangtung | 150.0 | 270.0 | 30.0 | 1,500 |
| Kwangsi | 80.0 | 238.0 | 20.0 | 1,000 |
| Szechwan | 530.0 | 150.0 | — | 1,333 |
| Kweichow | 185.0 | 150.0 | 18.0 | 400 |
| Yunnan | 160.0 | 100.0 | 30.0 | 1,000 |

SOURCE: *Water Conservancy*, No. 9 (Sept. 14, 1957)
* The total also includes some small figures for municipalities which are omitted here.

Because the problem of management was underestimated, many projects did not play their economic role in irrigation and flood prevention. Because of improper management, many projects met with accidents, damaging the materials of the people and the state.[14]

The above comments from such an expert reveal Communist China's unrealistic claims of expansion of effective

[14] *Ibid.*

irrigation in 1958 as well as the great problems she must face in the efficient use of the limited amount of available water.

## V. UNDERGROUND WATER SUPPLIES

Data on prospective supplies of underground water appear to be meager and claims of irrigation ambiguous.[15] With regard to wells, the Communists asserted that in 1956 there were four times as many as in 1949; while the number of water wheels had increased from 300,000 to 1,500,000. In addition, it is claimed that the area irrigated by wells had increased about five million hectares in the provinces of Honan, Shantung, and Hopei—well-known wheat and cotton provinces. But it was admitted in Hopei, that as more wells were dug, less and less water was obtainable from each well. In 1956, 40 per cent of all the wells were providing an inadequate amount of water for the area intended.

Total available mechanical power for irrigation and drainage at the end of 1960 was given as six million horsepower. But currently there are serious limitations in the supply of steel, fuel, and lubricating oil. As a result, the Communists are considering cutting a link between the Yangtze and the Yellow River. This, however, cannot be expected to be of benefit within the next several years since it would require an enormous amount of manpower and materials. For this reason, the Communists are making a major effort to find more underground water although such an attempt also requires deep drilling and extensive amounts of mechanical equipment if they are not to be faced with limited supplies of water at shallow levels.

With regard to underground water, Krylov states:

It is worth mentioning that according to the figures of the water ministry of the C.P.R. underground water is used for the irrigation of over 2 million hectares of land which are

[15] Krylov, *op. cit.*, p. 4.

expected to be increased to 4 million by 1967. That would require a colossal volume of underground water with a discharge up to 2,000 cubic meters per second, that is, half again as much the average annual discharge of the Hwan Ho [Yellow River] . . .[16]

The solution of the irrigation problem in China depends to a considerable extent on the artificial control of the subsoil waters by a complex system of ameliorative measures. In particular, much work has yet to be done in channeling off the subsoil water in certain areas of China by the construction of a water-catchment and drainage network, afforestation along the irrigation canals, etc., within the complex framework of agro-technical and hydro-technical ameliorative operations.[17]

It is thus apparent that large scale planning is one of the prerequisites for the extensive expansion of underground waters sources for irrigation purposes. Mere installation of pumps will not suffice and more attention must be given to the quality and quantity of the underground water. Practical estimates based on scientific mapping of potential sources of underground water, however, are meager.

The figures quoted by Krylov are considerably lower than those quoted above, illustrating the problem of reconciling official and semi-official announcements.

## VI. REPORTED ESTIMATES OF POTENTIAL EXPANSION OF EFFECTIVELY IRRIGATED AREAS

To expand irrigated areas effectively, adequate drainage must go hand in hand with such plans. Adequate drainage and flood control will also help to reduce waterlogging, a major problem in large areas.

It is hoped that this brief catalogue of officially planned improvements will facilitate a general check on future progress. In view of the lack of detailed expert estimates of potentially irrigable areas in China's pre-Communist period,

[16] *Ibid.*
[17] *Ibid.*

we have no clear basis for judging the feasibility of the apparently erroneous claims of expected expansion of areas under irrigation set forth by the Communist plans. The following is a brief summary of planned expansion:

### Summary of Main Projects

Hwai River Project [18]
    (between the Yellow River and the Yangtze, covering part of 3 provinces—Honan, Anhwei, and Kiangsu)

| | | |
|---|---|---|
| Cultivated area | 12,600,000 | hectares |
| Irrigated area | 2,100,000 | hectares |
| Irrigable area | 10,500,000 | hectares |
| Target 1957 | | |
| Cultivated area | 13,600,000 | hectares |
| Annual surface flow on average recorded at | 36,600,000 | cubic meters |
| Ordinary year | 31,900,000 | cubic meters |
| Sufficient for | 5,200,000 | cubic meters if regulated |
| | 19,700,000 | cubic meters only sufficient for |
| | 3,600,000 | hectares |
| Yellow River [19] | | |
| Irrigated area | 1,100,000 | hectares reported |
| Annual flow approximately | 47,000,000,000 | cubic meters |
| Irrigated area could be | 7,700,000 | hectares if utilized |
| Hai River [20] | | |
| Improved irrigation and drainage will affect | 2,000,000 | hectares |

[18] Hydro-electricity, op. cit., No. 4 (April 14, 1957), p. 12.
[19] Teng Tze-hui, address to National People's Congress, Peking, July 1955.
[20] Report on Hai Ho, Conservancy Commission in Geographical Knowledge (June 1958), p. 13.

*Other Irrigation Works* [21]

| | |
|---|---|
| Minor irrigation works in North and Northwest China | 200,000 hectares |
| Yangtze San Chienkow Dam irrigation capacity | 800,000 hectares |
| Yangtze Gorge Dam project in process of preparation | |
| Works in South China having most to do with flood control | |
| Above total involves plans to expand irrigated areas by some | 17,000,000 hectares |

If we add to the above another four million hectares due to the expanded use of underground water mentioned by Krylov, we get an impressive total increase of 21 million hectares. Krylov, however, believed that much of this would be needed to supplement shortages in river supply. We should, therefore, discount the above to some extent.

According to our calculations (Table 2), with the use of somewhat questionable official data on the rice area and estimates of other crops irrigated—and allowing for double cropping—only some 36 million hectares of irrigated land was required by 1958. This figure represents an increase of 11.2 million over the prewar adjusted *Statistical Monthly* figure of 24.8 million but is less than the *LU* figure of 39.4 million hectares. If the above increases can be achieved, the total would then be 58 million hectares or about 53 per cent of the cultivated area. But as the above are government sponsored projects of medium and small scale, an additional large allowance can be made for cooperative projects as shown in Table 3.

As the list of projects implies full use of available water in North China, to increase it further means diverting surplus water from the Yangtze River to the Yellow River Basin.

[21] *People's Daily*, May 26, 1954.

This would be a major undertaking in the history of irrigation in view of the gigantic engineering problems and it is
believed that such an undertaking would take a few decades
to achieve results. Nevertheless, according to Shih-tu Hsu,[22]
a noted authority on irrigation, the potentiality is there and
more than 12 million hectares of the flood plain in North
China might be benefited by supplemental irrigation if the
diversion and storage of some 36,000 million cubic meters
could be carried out in addition to other plans, the irrigated
land in China might be increased to some 60 per cent which,
in turn, would permit a greatly expanded use of chemical
fertilizer. The value of irrigation to increased yields is inter-
dependent with the use of chemical fertilizer. The length of
time necessary to work out this required expansion depends
on huge amounts of capital and an adequate supply of
trained engineers and agricultural extension agents. Even
should these conditions be met, this project, in the opinion
of the writer, may well take at least 20 years.

## VII. SUMMARY AND CONCLUSION

The importance of expanding irrigation in Communist
China is brought into sharp focus by the disastrous effects
of the 1959–61 drought which centered in the northern
provinces where some 50 per cent of the claimed increase in
irrigation since 1952 had occurred. Deficient water supplies
also affected other areas during this period. It is, therefore,
evident that a much greater expansion in water supplies is
needed to assure food crops for the growing population,
especially in North China.

Although reports on irrigation developments in Communist China since 1949 are conflicting, there seems to be
some convergence in regard to extent and effectiveness. The

[22] Former water conservancy specialist in prewar China; now serving at
Taiwan University in the same capacity.

officially reported figure for 1949 (Table 1) was absurdly low; it continued low until 1955 and then suddenly jumped to 38 million irrigated hectares in 1956.

Because the prewar adjusted figures as given in the *Statistical Monthly* differ from those in the *LU* Survey by Buck (Table 1) for the level of land irrigation, it is difficult to make a comparison between the pre- and postwar periods. The Communist definition of irrigated land, at least up to 1956, may not have covered some of the types included in the *LU* Survey. While the definition set forth in 1956 seems to cover all forms, other statements by officials use the term "effective irrigation."

Figures after 1956 are very tenuous and indicate a probable total of 40 million irrigated hectares by 1960, although the effectiveness of this irrigation is questionable. With the significant recovery in agricultural planning and improved crop conditions, the area irrigated by 1964 may have reached some 46 to 50 million hectares. The potential increase in food grain, other factors being normal, might reach 10 to 15 million metric tons. More recently, significant increases in electrical pumping facilities have also occurred in local areas.

It is possible during the next 10 to 30 years that certain large-scale projects which now account for only a small percentage of the increased irrigation could go far in increasing and stabilizing the output of food grain to meet the needs of the growing population as well as provide products for export if these projects are actively supported by the necessary financial outlay encompassing a huge labor expenditure on engineering planning. Such an expansion in irrigation, however, must be accompanied by a similar one in the use of chemical fertilizer if a permanent increase in crop yields is to be obtained. Without such an expansion in both water resources and use of chemical fertilizer, crop increases—especially in North China—may fall seriously short of Communist China's needs in the next ten years.

## GLOSSARY

CATTY   One catty (*shih chin*) equals 0.5 kilogram.

CROP AREA   The land area devoted to crops. It is synonymous with cultivated land unless otherwise designated.

CROP HECTARES   A measure of the number of crops grown on the same land successively in one year.

DOUBLE CROPPING   Two crops in one year, which is also considered as multiple cropping.

EIGHT AGRICULTURAL AREAS   These areas of the 22 provinces were delineated in the *Land Utilization in China* study for their homogeneity primarily with respect to climate, soil, and types of crops.

*HSIANG*   Township.

*HSIEN*   County.

*MOW (SHIH MOU)*   A unit of land equal to 1/15 of a hectare.

MULTIPLE CROPPING   Two or more crops grown successively in one year on the same land.

PROVINCES   The 22 provinces under control of the Nationalist Government, and not including Manchuria, Sikang, and Sinkiang were as follows:

| | | | |
|---|---|---|---|
| Anhwei | Hopei | Kwangsi | Shantung |
| Chahar | Hunan | Kwangtung | Shensi |
| Chekiang | Hupei | Kweichow | Suiyuan |
| Chinghai | Kansu | Ningsia | Szechwan |
| Fukien | Kiangsi | Shansi | Yunnan |
| Honan | Kiangsu | | |

# Index